When Plimsoll arrives, tell him
that Veronica used to be
engaged to Freddie

Lord Emsworth's Annotated Whiffle

Lord Emsworth's Annotated Whiffle

The Care of the Pig
by Augustus Whiffle

Edited By
~~JAMES HOGG~~

For the author's
god daughter Sophia,
with love

James
10 . X . 12

MICHAEL JOSEPH   LONDON

First published by Popgood and Grooly 1898
Revised edition 1915
This edition 1991

MICHAEL JOSEPH LTD
Published by the Penguin Group
27 Wrights Lane, London W8 5TZ, England
Viking Penguin, a division of Penguin Books USA Inc.,
375 Hudson Street, New York, New York 10014, USA
Penguin Books Australia Ltd, Ringwood, Victoria, Australia
Penguin Books Canada Ltd, 10 Alcorn Avenue, Toronto, Ontario, Canada M4V 3B2
Penguin Books (NZ) Ltd, 182–190 Wairau Road, Auckland 10, New Zealand

Penguin Books Ltd, Registered Offices: Harmondsworth, Middlesex, England

First published in Great Britain 1991

Copyright © James Hogg 1991

Printed in England by Clays Ltd, St Ives plc
Filmset in Monophoto Van Dijck

A CIP catalogue record for this book is available from the British Library
ISBN 0 7181 3476 1

The moral right of the author has been asserted

Illustrations on pp. 18, 21, 25, 30, 50, 75, 95
and 122 are reproduced by permission of
the Ann Ronan Picture Library

Contents

Preface

WHEN Lord Emsworth's annotated copy of *The Care of the Pig* came into my possession, its 756 pages seemed more than a little daunting. On dipping into it, however, I saw that with drastic pruning a new edition could find a place on the shelves of the modern reader. Whiffle was the leading man in his field during the Edwardian era. He ranged widely — too widely by today's standards — over the history and practice of pig-keeping, but between the longueurs there was much to instruct and enlighten.

In deciding what to keep and what to discard, I have made it a rule to steer clear of technical detail. No one knew better than Whiffle how to run a piggery, and when it came to passing on his skills he gave full measure. Fortunately he was also a lifelong student of pig-human relations, and it is his observations on that neglected corner of experience which have so much to teach us about the *mores* of another age.

In contrast, his guidance on theoretical matters, often continued for page after page, has not withstood the passage of time. Wolff-Lehman's complex tabulations of feed-to-weight ratios, once slavishly followed by all the top breeders, contain little to divert us today; they, together with the long section on the properties of bran mash, have had to go.

There may be some *aficionados* of the pig who cannot have too much of that sort of thing, and will regret the loss. However, I believe the general reader has been better served by my concentrating on the anecdotal and philosophical side of Whiffle's work.

Whiffle himself revised *The Care of the Pig* for a new edition in 1915. He made some concessions to changing circumstances, perhaps most arrestingly in his contention that pigs had played a decisive role in the causes of the First World War. Essentially, however, it remained the same book as when it had first appeared in 1898.

In the preface to that edition, Whiffle had acknowledged his distinguished predecessors Youatt, Long, Low and Sydney, but that did not prevent mutterings about plagiarism in the narrow world of the pig dogmatists of the day. In his 1915 preface Whiffle met these objections in characteristically head-on fashion. He bluntly suggested that Youatt and the others had taken most of their information from his uncle, Sir Craster Whiffle, and that if there were any plagiarists he knew where to look. We shall probably never know the truth.

None of this mattered in the least to Lord Emsworth, of that we can be sure. *The Care of the Pig* was his favourite reading, and whenever life at Blandings Castle threatened to become too interesting he would retire to the library and lose himself in Whiffle's prose. In case there are readers who need reminding about any of the references in his marginal notes, the following list may be useful:

Beach:	Butler at Blandings Castle.
Belford:	James Belford was married to Lord Emsworth's niece Angela. Knowledgeable about American pig-keeping methods.
Connie:	Lord Emsworth's sister, Lady Constance, the formidable chatelaine of Blandings.
The Empress:	Lord Emsworth's prize pig, oft-times winner at the Shropshire Agricultural Show.
Freddie:	Lord Emsworth's not very bright younger son.
Galahad:	Lord Emsworth's brother Gally, otherwise the Hon. Galahad Threepwood. *Bon vivant*, and man of tireless resource when things go wrong.

The Pelican:	Club to which Gally and fellow spirits belonged in their youth.
Plimsoll:	Tipton Plimsoll was the rich American suitor of Veronica Wedge, daughter of Colonel and Lady Hermione Wedge (q.v.), and niece of Lord Emsworth. The *aide-mémoire*, jotted by Lord Emsworth on the flyleaf of this volume, should have read: 'When Plimsoll arrives, *don't* tell him that Veronica was once engaged to Freddie.'
Monica Summers:	The Empress's attendant for a time.
Veronica:	See under Plimsoll.
Egbert Wedge:	Colonel Wedge was married to Lord Emsworth's sister, Lady Hermione.
Wellbeloved:	Lord Emsworth's longest-serving pigman.

– JAMES HOGG, March 1991

I

Sir Craster's Manifesto

'YOU may discover all that is necessary of a man's character from his attitude to pigs.'

How many times have I heard my uncle, Sir Craster Whiffle, utter those words at the dinner table, and watched the company fall into a thoughtful silence. Often they would be people to whom such a proposition had never occurred; the kind who, as my uncle used to say, 'thought the only difference between pigs and pork was apple sauce'. One could tell from the way the conversation entered a subdued phase for some time afterwards that his words had gone home.

Sir Craster held that the world was divided between those who had given serious attention to the subject of pigs, and the remainder. There were more of the latter than he would wish, but his refusal to be disheartened was an example to others. Whenever he encountered a clear case of ignorance, he was tireless in correcting it.

He might, for instance, while staying with friends, find himself in the company of the daughter of the house, her mind filled with the stuff and nonsense of the adolescent female. Instead of ignoring the child, he would take the opportunity to educate her, over a period of hours if necessary, in a better appreciation of the pig.

In order not to bore her, he would leave for later those particulars which might prove too much for the beginner, and kindle her interest by focusing upon mucking out,

Freddie and his friends no interest whatsoever. Not a thought in their heads anything that really matters

preparing swill and so forth. By the time he had moved on to the principles of cross-breeding, his young interlocutor would be open-mouthed at the wealth of information imparted by her kindly guide. In the end, he told me, her eyes would be quite closed in the effort of concentration.

My uncle died suddenly at the age of ninety-three, after superintending the serving of a favourite sow, Queen of the Fairies. It had been his wish to be taken while among his herd (it would not have occurred to him to keep any but the native pig of Lincolnshire, where there have been Whiffles for eight hundred years). Before he died, leaving me six boars, a hundred breeding sows and his collection of pig-books, Sir Craster placed the continuation of his life's work in my hands. Loyal to his memory, I regard the advancement of pig-breeding as a solemn trust, to be shouldered with pride and defended with vigour.

One obligation I inherited from Sir Craster was to counter the slanderous nonsense on the subject of pigs put about by those who should know better. Among them I include the French author Buffon, who, in his *Histoire Naturelle et Particulière* (trans. Finch-Fussell) described the animal thus: 'All its habits are gross, all its tastes unclean'.

In view of the makeshift conditions of pig-keeping he was accustomed to through accident of birth, this statement of Buffon's should be sent smartly back to the other side of the Channel. Condemning a whole species, on the basis of the unfortunate beasts whose fate it was to be born in his country, is not justice as we know it in Great Britain. Since the pig's powers of reply are confined to an uncomprehending grunt, I take up the cudgels on its behalf thus: given a sty eight foot square, half open to the sky, and with food slopped anywhere, even a French naturalist might find his standards slipping.

No idea such a state of affairs existed. Shudder to think Empress treated in this way

Let me quote instead the words of a trusty Englishman of the sixteenth century: 'The hog is the cleanliest of all creatures. He will voide his foul humoures as far as he can get forth'. In a number of cases that is not very far, and thus has arisen the fallacy that a pig can be kept in circumstances more suited to a swarm of blue-bottles.

Alas, it is not only the French who are guilty. The English author Floodgate, in his *Treatise On Cattle*, complained of the pig's 'furious lust and eager gluttony'. I do not see that the lust of the pig is any more furious than that of the rest of the animal kingdom. If Floodgate knew a species whose habits in this regard were a topic for the drawing room, I should like to hear of it. The creature itself is the best judge of the way it goes about the matter, and needs no advice from literary men.

As for gluttony, Providence has given the pig a digestive system which any fair-minded person would view with envy. The hearty appetite so pilloried by the ill-informed is simply the result of superior internal arrangements. It is these which allow the species to be less particular than certain confounded authors would like. I only hope that Floodgate, now alas dead, enjoyed his food as well.

Many in the pig world considered it bad form that an authority on cattle should have gone out of his way to insult another inhabitant of the farmyard. It ill became a man who may have known all there was to be known about cows, but showed himself to be lamentably out of his depth in the piggery.

Certainly—

Mrs Whiffle tells me I express myself too vigorously about the vapourings of authors who may no longer be living, but I owe it to Sir Craster Whiffle to pursue quackery wherever I find it. As I often heard him say: 'Never trust a man who talks a better pig than he keeps' (many of his maxims appeared in the monthly article he wrote for sixty-three years in the *Lindsey and Kesteven Pig-Breeder*, under the heading 'Notes from the Sty').

There is a further misconception I must set straight at once. From time to time it is put about that there is something inherently amusing about pigs. I cannot emphasize too strongly the mischief this belief can cause. I am something of a humorist myself, but there is a time and place for such things. For example, while staying at the Pig-Breeders' Club in Brook Street, W., I have often had the smoking room in an uproar.

I recall showing members an advertisement in the newspaper, which read as follows: 'An interesting gilt-framed oil painting of a sow in need of restoration'. You see, while trying to suggest that the painting needed restoring, the advertiser had implied that it was the sow which was in a state of disrepair. The fact that no owner would commission a portrait of his pig except in the peak of condition merely added to the hilarity.

awfully good!

Having put paid to the idea that I am incapable of mirth if the circumstances warrant it, I return to my word of warning (or perhaps I should say *revenons à nos cochons* – a *bon mot* for which I am indebted to the late Sir Craster Whiffle. When he first introduced it at the Pig-Breeders' Club, not all the members understood it. On hearing the explanation, however, they laughed as heartily as the rest). No, it is the tendency to see the pig as a source of merriment which I deplore.

An instance springs to mind which has been written up in a flippant fashion in one of the university magazines. A trio of undergraduates contrived to import a young boar into the Reading Room of the British Museum. It may be asked how they introduced a farmyard animal without the librarians noticing. The answer is simple. The devils had got themselves up as workmen, adopted a low manner of speech, and claimed to have been summoned by the Clerk of Works to clear the drains.

Gulled by these 'plumbers', the authorities gave scarcely a thought to the large box they were carrying, apparently full of tools of the trade. The intruders made for a quiet corner of the Reading Room, released their captive, and left hurriedly. Having abandoned their disguises in the gentlemen's cloakroom, they were in time to revisit the scene of the crime dressed as respectable undergraduates, and see the result of their folly.

Anyone who has visited the Reading Room of the British Museum will know that it is unsuited to the squeals, grunts and other indicators of a pig out of its element. Dining at the Athenaeum some weeks later I ran into Professor Salthouse, who had been present during the disturbance. He told me it had been several days before he felt able to resume his researches into the configuration of particles. The Revd Claud Pomeroy, author of *Monastic Reform 959–970*, was bitten on the ankle as the pig darted between the legs of readers at their desks. Other scholars, many of them elderly, had to be treated for shock.

The identity of the villains became known after they had the gall to publish their own account of it. In the Pig-Breeders' Club it was adjudged a sending-down offence, but they were let off with a gating, the universities having abandoned all pretence at keeping order. It is fortunate for these trouble-makers that my uncle is not still among us. A letter to *The Times* from Sir Craster would have given them more to think about than any gating there ever was.

I trust that disposes of the idea that levity has any place in a study of the pig. Having outlined the guiding principles Sir Craster left to us, I now turn to the history of an animal which has deservedly been called the 'Corinthian' of the farmyard.

II
The Pig Honoured
in the Chase

WHEN writing in the *Lindsey and Kesteven Pig-Breeder*,
Sir Craster Whiffle came down heavily on dabbling
historians of the pig, who had never clapped eyes on a wild
boar. 'It is as if Mrs Beeton had gone through life without
eating game pie', he declared. In reviewing the species in
the natural state I have had to pick my way through a
mixed bag of authors, some of whose accounts verge on the
downright unbelievable. I leave the reader to place them in
whichever category he prefers.

As a devotee of the chase during my days in India, I can
only applaud the hunting spirit to be found in classical tales,
once the human carnage is got out of the way and due
attention given to tracking the boar. One must regret that
an element of the former creeps into the account of the
fourth labour of Hercules.

Admittedly under provocation, he massacres a party of
meddlers who are holding up his pursuit of the Erymanthian
boar. However, a more edifying note is introduced when he
corners the beast in a snowdrift, an eventuality I never
encountered in Indian conditions. As decreed, the boar is
brought back alive and presented to the king, a shameless
coward who hides in a jar until it can be released at a safe distance.

Many of these classical fighting men seem at one time or
another to have engaged in tussles with the pig, some
coming off better than others. The Cremmyon Sow, which

had been disrupting agriculture near Corinth, was soon seen
off by Theseus. On the other hand, Odysseus was scarred
for life when he got the worst of the argument with his
particular quarry, and Adonis, by all accounts a thorough-
going sportsman, had the stuffing knocked out of him in an
encounter with a venomous old tusker. However, I am sure
he shared my view that if you go out after boar you must
accept the consequences in a spirit of give and take.

In those days, being on active service was a simple matter
of engaging the enemy at close quarters, and boar-hunting
was first-class training. If you could look one of these
brutes that Homer talks about in the eye, the average foot
soldier held no terrors at all:

> Roused by the hounds' and hunters' mingling cries,
> The savage from his leafy shelter flies.
> With fiery glare his sanguine eye-balls shine,
> And bristles high impale his horrid chine.

Say what you like about Homer, and I confess that much of
what I waded through for the purpose of this book was
wearisome in the extreme, he must have been a hunting
man. The above lines bring back old times on the Deccan
plain as clear as yesterday; but I will touch on my own
experiences in the field later.

The wild boar is a formidable-looking customer, whose
main properties as an adversary are a murderous pair of
tusks, a vile temper, and an ability to move like greased
lightning. He seems to fly rather than run, and not merely
for a dash into the nearest available cover. In open country
he can keep it up as long as you like.

The boar comes armed with a pair of rapiers in the lower
jaw, which inflict maximum damage as he brings them up
underneath the enemy in a tearing and ripping action. Being
on the wrong end of this manoeuvre is to be avoided
wherever possible. The tusk is as sharp as a razor, and
crescent-shaped so as to gain full benefit from the upwards

offensive thrust. I have known one, extracted after prolonged boiling of the head, to measure no less than $12\frac{1}{8}$ inches. Frankly these fellows who cut a dash out fox-hunting, and think they are mighty brave, should wait till they have fallen foul of a malignant old boar with the light of battle in his eyes. Then they might have something worth talking about.

I place in the same category the French author M. Buffon, referred to earlier. From the safety of his study he commented thus: 'The boar strikes, lunges and tears, but without agility or address'. If circumstances had allowed it, I could have introduced Buffon to some specimens of whose agility and address he would have spoken highly, had he survived the experience.

To those who complain that the wild pig is no beauty, I would point to the practicality of its salient features. The hideous visage is elongated to allow it to grub for roots without falling on its head. The small, sunken eyes, peevish though they may appear during hostilities, are safe from damage as it hurtles through the brushwood thickets of its forest home — the boar will not step aside for anything living. I have known one knock down a camel, and run full tilt into an elephant. Being no fool, it wants to die of old age like anyone else, but once crossed it is the most belligerent devil you could wish to meet.

It is a matter of considerable regret that the wild pig no longer roams the wooded regions of this country. As a responsible landowner, William the Conqueror was concerned at the declining number in his own day. His response — a decree that anyone found hunting boar in the royal forests was to have his eyes put out — may have been somewhat drastic, but taken all in all was an outstanding success. Stocks began to build up, and His Majesty, a great sportsman to whom the ban did not apply, was able to hunt again with a clear conscience.

Later, of course, a relaxation of penal policy was allowed to creep in, and once more hunting by all and sundry went unpunished. That was the end of the boar in this country, but for a brief revival at the instigation of King Charles I, who imported a small breeding population from Germany and ran them in the New Forest. This excellent plan fell foul of the Cromwellian party in the Civil War. The boar attracted the interest of bands of Puritans in the neighbour-hood, who reinforced their iron rations with as much wild pork as they could lay their hands on. The work of these scavengers took its toll. Too late to benefit from the protec-tion of William the Conqueror, the herd was soon no more.

*Perhaps consult Whiffle
introduce wild boar
Friar's Wood.
Practical difficulties —
    Connie etc.*

III
My Own Experience
of the Boar

DESPITE the extinction of the species in our country, all is not lost for the British sportsman. With service in India open to any young man of spirit, there is no reason why all who choose should not pit themselves against the pig in his eastern haunts. When I joined Skinner's Horse in '74, the duties of a subaltern in the Indian Army could be seen off in an hour-and-a-half, and during the rest of the day he could hunt to his heart's content.

Very few of life's activities go entirely according to plan, and this business of chasing the boar out east is no exception. Your Indian villager is a willing character, who means well, but cannot see very far beyond his nose. Mutinies, even in neighbouring towns, pass him by. Legislative councils might as well not exist. All that matters to the simple fellow is his family, his cows, and the prospects for rain. This can make him something of a liability in the hunting field.

The mounting of a successful *battue* in the sugar plantations requires the deployment of a party of beaters who know what they are doing. The natives, contracted for the equivalent of about fourpence a day, make a reasonable show of interest at first, but either become restive at the lack of early success, or panic once in proximity to the boar. Accidents will happen and beaters may receive a few cuts and bruises, but they are seldom serious, and hardly warrant the headlong flight which often accompanies the first hint of danger. If ever one of the hunting party is unhorsed he can look in vain for support from his native employees. They will be heading for home leaving him to his fate.

However, instead of closing with the luckless sportsman, the boar will sometimes set off after the absconding beaters. With his superior speed he soon overhauls the stragglers. Then, by running his head between the fugitives' knees, he gives them a graze or two in a tender spot. Few of the party escape a rip before they are relieved of their pursuer.

This failure to enter into the spirit of the chase is quite transformed when the villagers call on the Army to deal with a boar whose criminal tendencies have become a nuisance to them. These individuals take up their quarters on the outskirts of the village, or even in the plots behind the houses. We would bring four or five elephants for the purpose, and all concerned would have excellent sport (though a degree of ill-will was generated when it proved impossible to stop the elephants helping themselves to bananas as they passed through the garden plantations).

We would have many a lively dash round the village, up the streets and back again, with natives flying in all directions, or clustering in trees to see themselves rid of the suburban boar which was plaguing them. They were never as mustard keen at a meet in open country.

It is a grave mistake to beat out of pig coverts in June. The sows bolt, and striped squeakers of all sizes from the rat upwards scatter like gunshot. It is better to stick to the fringes and locate your solitary boar, who is no more fond of a screeching family than the rest of us. Indeed a prickly temperament is a characteristic of the type. The late Punch Pauncefote, who probably did more for pig-sticking in Bengal than any man living, once saw a cantankerous old boar come out of the jungle near Patkabaree, attack a bullock-cart with a few well-placed cuts, and then trot sulkily back again. Punch put it down either to toothache, unrequited love, or the stresses of family life.

Punch acquired his name because of an incident which occurred when he pursued a boar into a cactus patch.

Unfortunately, as he was attempting to change direction, his horse backed into a particularly vicious piece of vegetation. In the ensuing melodrama Punch was thrown to the ground, and suddenly found himself at the mercy of an enraged boar seeking revenge. However, when the brute charged, Punch landed him a violent blow on the snout with his clenched fist, and made good his escape while the assailant's eyes were still watering. He was always known as Punch from that day on.

The adventure did not affect him in the slightest degree, and he was out hunting the following day as though nothing had happened. I have known cases, however, when an altercation with the boar can have the most damaging consequences. Colonel Daines Bulkinhorn, after a distinguished showing at Tel el-Kebir, quite went to pieces over an encounter with a herd of masked African boar, or wood swine. Having gone out alone on a jungle reconnaissance, Colonel Bulkinhorn unwittingly disturbed a whole troop of the creatures, who left him in no doubt that his presence was resented. The wood swine is a hideous specimen with a fleshy excrescence on each side of the face, giving it an air of menace fully borne out by its disposition in the wild. The natives of central Africa are adamant that they would infinitely rather confront a hungry lion.

In his predicament Bulkinhorn had no choice but to take refuge in the nearest bago-bago tree, as the furious boar snapped at his heels. The bago-bago is not a robust growth (the natives use its branches as a fly-swat), and as a former heavyweight champion of Sandhurst he was in dread of the tree snapping under his weight, and leaving him at the mercy of his custodians. With erected bristles and eyes glinting with rage they held their ground for hour after hour, their habit of excitedly clashing their teeth together adding to the discomfiture of their captive.

It was not until nightfall that instinct drove them to seek out their sleeping quarters, and he was able to creep cautiously back to camp. Alas, Bulkinhorn never entirely got over the incident. At any rate, he retired from the army soon afterwards, and became, I understand, one of the leading exponents of needlepoint in Hampshire.

One may easily come to grief in the hunting field through no fault of one's own. Archie Stoope-Funnell was landed once with a spavined horse, which compounded the felony by stepping in a porcupine hole just as they drew abreast of their quarry. In the resulting purler, Archie was thrown across the back of the flying boar. It punished his presumption with a swift thrust before going on its way.

For many years afterwards Archie suffered twinges around the base of the backbone in cold weather. The horse meanwhile had taken to its heels and was only recaptured with difficulty. Such was the impression left by the incident on its limited powers of understanding that from then on it fled at the sight of a recumbent farmyard sow. Of course as a hunter it was no longer worth a farthing, and had to be put on ceremonial duties.

A less intimidated horse will sometimes present its croup to the boar and kick vigorously. The difficulty is that when once it has embarked on this show of spirit, it seldom knows when to leave off. Long after the danger is over the horse may still be seen exercising its heels in lively fashion, eventually spilling its exasperated rider in the process.

Even greater havoc reigns when the studs take it into their heads to declare war. I have more than once seen horses, regardless of a hog right under their noses, engage in a furious kicking match with the intention of seeing off a rival. The riders are obliged to dismount, under their own steam or otherwise, and make the best escape they can from the double hazard of hoof and tusk.

On one notable occasion the wrath of the human female added a new ingredient to the perils of the chase. We were on a Tent Club hunt, Poona way, and were camped on the edge of a village. Tiger Pitt-Smollett was in the middle of his ablutions, with a face full of soap, when a disgruntled native woman appeared at the door of his tent, seized one of his Bengal spears, and announced her intention in colourful terms of running him through with it. Discretion being the better part of valour, he made excellent time round the field with the agitated spearswoman in hot pursuit.

Fortunately the cooks, who had been preparing breakfast, saw the incident and managed to secure the aggressor before her mission could be accomplished. I could only agree when the chief cook described the affair as 'a bad business'. It was never established what her grievance was, though it seemed possible that she had mistaken Tiger for a district officer who had found against her in a dispute with her mother-in-law. Being the sportsman that he was, Tiger insisted that the charge be reduced from attempted murder to disturbing the peace.

The Tent Club is a first-class institution, as long as it is properly run. Some have a committee; others not. Personally I have never seen a committee that was worth a rap in any affair of this life. My advice to those asked to be Hon. Sec. of a Tent Club is to decline unless given full executive powers. Have a committee by all means, but strictly *honoris causa*; then you can ignore it.

Another useful pointer is that a Tent Club meet should be for gentlemen participants only. It is hard enough to get latecomers to keep quiet when beating out a cover is in progress. They invariably wish to inform anyone within earshot about the time they have had getting there and so forth; any skylarking from lady followers would finally put paid to sport for the day.

Tent Club rules are not always given the respect they should be, particularly in the way members go about measuring their boar. I always imposed a fine of a dozen champagne for a breach of regulations. The procedure is quite straightforward. Take a line between the perpendiculars from the withers to the heel. However, when the boar is carried back suspended along a pole it is apt to measure more by the time it reaches camp than it did when it started out. Some hardened sinners, intent on claiming a club record, were known to bribe their coolies to take a circuitous route home for this express purpose. When unmasked, this crime called for the strict imposition of the fine, and hearty Tent Club celebrations at the expense of the miscreant.

After dinner it is the duty of the Hon. Sec. to write up the daily log. One of my colleagues, Stuffy Elbone, was a talented poet, and used to add a literary note to the log when the occasion seemed to call for it. This is but a sample of Stuffy's poetic skills:

> The tusker came down like a wolf on the fold;
> His ivories were gleaming like silver and gold.
> The glints of his eyes were like stars in the East;
> He charged like a Cossack, but now is deceased.

There can be few of us who have not seen midnight come and go while discussing which form of hunting is most to be preferred. For myself, whether after the boar, the buffalo or the rabbit, I think each the best at the time. Yet if pressed, I confess that none can equal the wild hog of India – an awesome foe and a noble prize.

Galahad always says Egbert Wedge went pig-sticking in his pyjamas. Have never liked to ask him

IV
Pig-keeping in Former Times

*Thank
Heaven
that it
was so!*

MANY thinkers have given their minds to the following
question. How was the gaunt, long-snouted boar, a
forest-dweller of peppery disposition, transformed into the
harmonious contours of the British pig, admired at all the
agricultural shows of Europe, the delicacy of the rich and
salvation of the poor?

Your typical pig-keeper has never been one for putting
pen to paper, and we are thus largely in the dark as to the
answer. However, the debt that is owed to the pioneering
pigmen of antiquity can never be forgotten. Though we
might scruple to invite them to dinner, let us not forget
that they too were friends of the pig. In cave and hovel an
alliance was forged of which we are the blessed legatees
today.

The story goes that pigs discovered the medicinal properties of the springs at Bath. No jury would hang a man on
the evidence, but according to Youatt, who is sound on
pigs, a certain tribal king of antiquity sent his son Baldred
to be educated abroad. When the lad returned to Britain he
was found to be leprous and was confined to the pesthouse,
which was no doubt even less salubrious then than it was
later.

While still a threat to public health, he absconded and
took a position as a swineherd near Bath, his employer
being presumably either a saint or a raving lunatic. We are
told that Baldred, whose attention to his duties seems to

have been deplorable, one day allowed the pigs to wander off in the middle of winter. On their return he was surprised to see them covered in mud, since it is the creatures' habit only to wallow in hot weather.

Skipping a torrent of circumstantial detail, we learn that the hot springs in which the pigs were rolling not only rid them of scabs and other eruptions, but also cured Baldred of his leprosy. On succeeding his father as king he founded the baths which have brought relief to the livers of millions, became a great philosopher and mathematician, and died respected by all. In 1699 pride in their supposed origins caused the citizens of Bath to erect a statue to Baldred in the spa, where I believe it stands today. In so far as pigs are addicted to rolling in mud, the story is authentic.

The post of swineherd, held briefly by Baldred, was never a popular one owing to the animal's aversion to being herded. Thus it generally fell to the idlest and stupidest fellow in the village. It is small wonder the pig gained a reputation as a public nuisance when its keeper was usually fast asleep under a tree, or worse still, in the comfort of his own bed. This gave rise to the old saw:

> While sluggarde swineherde sleeps at home,
> Both sowe and boare abroade will roame.

The taste of freedom sends a pig hurrying to the nearest piece of cultivated ground, where it sets to with a will, merrily ravaging the crops with the snout that nature has designed for the purpose. In the Middle Ages the pinner, or keeper of the pound, was continually rounding up animals allowed to stray by their loafing escort.

Helped or obstructed by the boys of the village, the pinner would lock the pigs in the pound, but his efforts were often to no avail. The loutish owners would wait until nightfall, break into the pound, and remove the inmates under cover of darkness to avoid the statutory fine. As if this were not bad enough for the good name of the animal, pig-keeping was the exclusive province of the dregs of society. Several centuries were to pass before public benefactors like Sir Craster Whiffle raised it to the peak of elevation it enjoys today.

It was the task of the swineherd, if awake, to run his charges in the neighbouring woods, where the villagers enjoyed the ancient right of pannage. The pigs were allowed to forage for acorns, mast and roots, though when damage to saplings became an anxiety to landowners, the pannage season had to be truncated. According to the old saw:

> For brackled* woodes there be no cure,
> While swine in pannage still endure.

Pannage. A swineherd watching his pigs eating acorns.

*Brackled is a word of indeterminate origin denoting 'damaged'. It may derive from the old German 'broch', meaning 'a stockman's goad suffering from long or excessive use'.

The breeding methods of the time lacked scientific principles of any kind. The pigs were given *carte blanche* in the matter, and preventing itinerant wild boars from pressing their attentions on the village sows would have taxed the liveliest swineherd. It is a wonder there was any improvement at all, when parenthood was decided by a chance encounter in the woods. The outcome of the union looked like a pig on short commons, quite lacking the fine hams and prodigious girth of our modern breeds.

My uncle's extensive library, now in my possession, throws light on some of the popular beliefs which attached to these rugged creatures. In *Natterjacke's Bestiary: Mysteries of Ye Animales*, the ancient writer Isaac Natterjacke describes how, at the full moon, pigs would gather in woodland clearings and form a circle; whereupon one of their number, usually the senior sow, would enter the ring and dance in the eerie half-light. 'Full many a time', he tells us, 'have I seen the queene pygge treade a measure in the forest glade, while her subjects do keep companie with chaunte and groane'. However, as Natterjacke claims a few pages further on to know of a boar which gave birth to a litter of eight, we need to approach his evidence with a good deal of caution.

Natterjacke is on firmer ground when he records the earnings of swineherds. It was felt that money only put temptation in the way of such wasters. They were therefore given the tails and intestines after slaughtering, and may have been overpaid at that. However, the curtailment of pannage, which had become a serious annoyance to the landed interest, slowly banished these erratic public servants from the scene.

Thus developed that valued institution whose benefits we know today – the house pig. Untroubled by the censure of his neighbours, who were doing the same thing, the cottager moved his pig near, and often into, his own living quarters. The need to refine the animal's social habits suddenly became pressing; it seems unlikely that these people were over-particular, but the company of a snappish and intractable pig in a confined space might trouble the most undemanding peasant.

So began the transformation of the breed into the benign and dignified creature we admire today. Obliged to fraternize with their pig, the improvers learned that the wayward brute would respond to a kindly word, a proffered morsel, or a scratch on the withers. While preferring to keep our own pigs at a respectable distance from the house, we may still warm to the thought of nightfall in the feudal cabin, with the snores of man and wife resonating euphoniously with those of their lodger.

When it came to selective breeding the primitive stockmen were oblivious as ever, and it took them several centuries to grasp the first principles. Now that procreation was no longer the result of a random coupling in the undergrowth, it was the time to seek out that *sine qua non* of breed improvement – an outstanding boar. But alas, these retarded agriculturalists lacked the wits for their task, and they merely transferred the random coupling to the backyard, using any boar they could come by. The cause of advanced pig-rearing was held up until men of sense at last took up the banner.

Being on more intimate terms with one's pig than we would choose today was not confined to the rustic classes, though the townsman may have jibbed at sharing his bedroom. Wandering swine were a familiar sight in the streets, sent out by their indigent owners to forage amid the rubbish. As one of the old writers put it: 'They are the husbandman's best scavenger, and the huswive's most wholesome sink. For their foode and living is that which would else rot in the yards, and make them beastlie'.

If it had ended there the animals might have been seen as operating a form of public service, but they began brazenly entering houses and helping themselves to the family provisions. The resulting animosity between neighbours led to many an appearance before the justices for assault.

I find the sound of the Empress sleeping an invaluable soporific in the late evening

The pigs made a further nuisance of themselves with their habit of molesting innocent by-standers. It is recorded that Sir Hugh Cholmely was bitten by a sow at the age of eight, though I have an idea the lad may have started the trouble. The origin of the name Boar's Hill in Oxford derives from a similar altercation. On being attacked by a nomadic pig near his college, a young scholar fought off his assailant by thrusting a book on philosophy down the beast's throat. It was not the first mortal thing to have choked on that particular diet.

Check with Gervase Cholmley his ancestor?

No one could be more devoted to the species than I (this has been confirmed by comments within the family circle), but the omnipresence of the pig in past centuries would have put my loyalties under severe stress. Innkeepers

The peasant's cottage, with pigs in residence

thought nothing of introducing one into a bed which had been found to be harbouring bugs as it was prepared for visitors. The pests rapidly transferred themselves onto the slumbrous pig, which was then removed, leaving the bed free of vermin.

However, human tolerance was stretched to breaking point on the occasion when, through an oversight, the sixteenth-century traveller Sir Nunc Verney was shown to his room while the pig was still in situ. The enraged knight is said to have seized a footstool and driven both pig and landlord from the scene with lusty blows, before retiring for the night satisfied at least that he would not be bitten to pieces as he slept.

Finally what have been called the Dark Ages of pig-rearing drew to a close. Men of destiny came forward ready to devote their lives to the service of a neglected animal. They were to bring order out of chaos, comeliness out of monstrosity, and turn ridicule into acclaim.

V
The Great Leap Forward

IT saddens a patriot to say so, but the turning point came
when the Chinese strain first penetrated the piggeries of
England. Its fattening properties had been known in parts of
Italy for generations, but our cautious native pigmen dis-
dained it (if they sufficiently stirred themselves to know of
its existence).

Sir Craster Whiffle had his own views as to how the
arrival of the Chinese pig in Europe, so momentous in its
consequences for us all, first came about (though family ties
do not blind me to the fact that his views have been chal-
lenged by rival scholars). Sir Craster based his theory upon a
journey along the old Silk Road undertaken by the father and
uncle of Marco Polo. These Venetian merchants, who must
have been of a different kidney from the merchants I saw on
a visit to Venice in '93, were taken up by the Mongolian
Emperor Kubla Khan. A most thoughtful host, he made it
his business to see that they got home without trouble.

The Emperor's grandfather, Genghis Khan, a far-sighted
ruler of great administrative gifts, had introduced a phil-
anthropic code of conduct enforceable by execution, called
the *yasa*. This controlled the wastes of Asia in a Pax Mon-
golica, and allowed the better type of traveller safe passage
back to the entrepôt stations of the Crimea. Without the
Emperor's *yasa* they would have been at the mercy of any
oriental cut-throat with an eye to the silks and spices they
were carrying in vast quantities.

It was Sir Craster's contention that they had other cargo besides. What could be more natural, he argued, than that these merchant venturers should have brought home a small breeding population of Chinese pigs? They would doubtless have seen the herd belonging to the hospitable Khan, and expressed their admiration of a well-rounded pig very different from the lean and rangy beast found in thirteenth-century Europe. It is as certain as anything can be that the Emperor would have pressed his guests to take some specimens back with them; and that the elder Polo and his brother would have at once seen the diversion and profit to be had from the gift.

Since Sir Craster published his theory in the *Lindsey and Kesteven Pig-Breeder*, certain professional faultfinders – a type referred to in parts of Lincolnshire as 'all brains and no bacon' – have objected that bringing pigs such a distance overland in ancient times would have been impossible. His reply was characteristic of a fearless and forthright countryman.

Having questioned the ability of his critics to take a pig five miles down the road to market, he printed a detailed itinerary between the Gobi Desert and Sevastopol, to show that the carrying of livestock by the Polos was eminently feasible. Sir Craster upheld his beliefs to the last. In an article written shortly before his death he pictured the Venetian pair, their caravan camped on the desolate steppes of Kazakhstan, sporting with their pets by the fireside while the slit-eyed sentinels of the *yasa* looked benignly on.

I don't doubt for a minute he was right

In later years, when the Chinese strain was firmly established in Europe, other travellers tried to trace the history of this influential pig. They found the Chinese uncommunicative on the subject, as on many others, and were forced to puzzle out its origins as best they could. The English traveller Tradescant Lay noted that Chinamen admired a round face and the smooth curvature of a tunbelly. When possible they cultivated these additions to beauty in themselves. Since the Chinese pig was fashioned on the same model, Lay concluded that it had been bred as near as ninepence to resemble its master; and according to his account the likeness did not end there, contrariness and obstinacy being the prevailing characteristics of both man and beast.

What I jocularly call the 'interlarding' of the Chinese with the Old English type was a mighty protracted business, because most of the old breeders were, in Lincolnshire idiom, eleven pigs to the dozen. They clung to the native animal long after progressive gentlemen had shown the way to improvement by combining the two strains. However, the criminal element soon spotted the difference, and landowners were rewarded for their efforts by an outbreak of larceny from the sty.

awfully neat. Try to remember that

Dwarf Chinese pigs

Gentlemen would keep the tastier pork of the improved pig for their own tables, recognizing that the labouring class was better served by the nourishing qualities of a coarser animal (it was now possible to separate layers of fat several inches thick to be salted down and it proved excellent sustenance for ploughmen and others).

This nicety was not given credit among those it was intended to benefit, and a rash of thefts occurred of the more delicately-flavoured porkers. Of course the scoundrels failed to realize that a refined diet was quite unsuited to their needs. However, the preference for a leaner cut soon spread, and now that an honest day's work seems a thing of the past, the demand for fat bacon has dwindled deplorably.

Not before time, pig-rearing in this country at last had men of vision at the helm. Since Britain led the world in all matters of any consequence, they saw no reason why the same supremacy should not apply in the case of pigs.

VI
The Principal Pig Breeds of England

ONCE the Englishman sets his mind to a task, the result is not in doubt. Whether it be seeing off foreign troublemakers, or conferring lustre on the pig, success can be depended upon. I have compared the advance of pig-rearing in this country to the rise of the nobility, so much do the two have in common. Like the great families of the shires, the aristocrats of the sty have qualities which have been the cause of comment throughout the world. Both speak volumes for the influence of breeding.

Not sure of this?

• The Small Black •

This meteor among pigs, illustrious but ill-fated, was the life's work of Squire Western (1767–1844). The Squire represented the agricultural interest in Parliament for forty-two years, and was also variously known as the Turkey or Stiffrump (a reference to a somewhat uncompromising seat in the hunting field). Lord Western, as he became, was the very model of the countryman, much like Mr Henry Chaplin in our own day. Having imported a black Neapolitan boar (derived from the Chinese type), he crossed it with selected sows in his native Essex. The result was for a time the most popular pig in England, but its constitution was less robust than that of its originator, the sows had the character of being bad nurses, and it went into a decline.

My father used to say Chaplin did more in Parliament for the landowner than all the rest of them put together

• *The Rudgwick* •

Another short-lived denizen of the sty, of interest because of
its exceptional size. Specimens were recorded weighing 116
stone. An eccentric Huntingdonshire breeder, Sir Almeric
Mudd, experimented with a Rudgwick boar and an Indian
jungle sow. The resultant progeny, born by Caesarian section, were crossed with the Improved Essex of Squire Western's strain, and by the time Sir Almeric went on to
introduce European wild boar into the equation, the multi-
plicity of size and colour, and the intractable nature of the
pigs, led him to abandon the project.

• *The Large White* •

Attenders at the Royal Agricultural Society's Exhibition at
Windsor in 1850 were electrified by the spectacle of pigs
such as had never been seen before. They were the work of
the celebrated Joseph Tuley, a member of the honest artisan
class in Yorkshire, who is spoken of in the same breath as
the very cream among gentleman breeders. With these mag-
nificent animals he founded the entire race of Large White
pigs, often called the Yorkshire breed.

Tuley's sow Matchless was honoured in a way which was
doubtless unique in the history of pig-keeping. She had a
litter which sold so well that Tuley was able to build
himself a weaver's cottage in Keighley out of the proceeds.
He called it Matchless House in recognition of her part in
the undertaking. This sow, and Tuley's boar Samson, were
the talk of pig circles for a generation. Their descendants
went round the world, their merits recognized by royal and
imperial owners, foreign potentates and governments.

In the terrible winter of 1860 one struggling tenant was
able to pay off the whole of his rent by selling progeny of a
sow of the Tuley strain. The Large White is a great favourite
with the better class of working man in Yorkshire and

Lancashire. Instead of idling away their time acquiring bad habits, these worthy mill-hands exhibit their pigs in a multitude of shows in both counties. Not content with ten or twelve to a litter, they breed for a great number of teats to gain maximum return for their efforts.

Tuley's pigs were taken up by Mr Wainman of Carhead, Yorks., whose animals have never been surpassed. Mr James Howard MP spoke of a feeling 'akin to regret' when he won Best Breeding Sow at the Royal Show against his early mentor Wainman. Mr Howard, a stickler for the highest standards, insisted on a boar with testicles set beneath the thickest part of the hams. When they protruded immediately below the tail he sold the boar to a less particular judge. He also insisted, quite rightly, that the tail should be long, shapely, and with a good tassel.

• *The Middle White* •

My uncle, Sir Craster Whiffle, told me how he once tried to fathom the genius of Joseph Tuley. In answer to his queries, Tuley replied: 'It's nobbut the breeding'. When Sir Craster pressed him to enlarge on this undeniable truth, Tuley forestalled further discussion with the comment: 'Stands to sense', which he repeated more than once. There the exchange ended. Many in the pig world would gladly give you Shakespeare for the recorded wisdom of such a prince among breeders, but the above is all we have of his *obiter dicta*.

At the Keighley Show in 1852 Tuley capped his display at the Royal two years earlier with a set of extraordinary pigs entered in the Large White class. Though they were out of his famous sows Matchless and Jenny Lind, the judges felt they were not of sufficient size for the class. Their merits were so outstanding that disqualification was out of the question (besides, Tuley had the reputation of being difficult when he considered himself wronged). The judges therefore decided that the prize-winning entry represented a new type, the Middle White.

As one of the most docile breeds in existence, the Middle White was tailor-made for the working man. Anyone who has had dealings with pigs knows they will move heaven and earth to get the wrong side of an enclosure, but any fence worthy of the name will hold a Middle White in check. They are so obliging that two sows will farrow in the same sty without a cross word. To attempt such a thing with the normal run of pigs would be to invite disaster.

Middle White sow and litter

• *The Small White* •

Characterized by their critics as animated tubs of lard, Small Whites are as much the product of the breeder's art as the pug or bulldog, which they resemble. The late Prince Consort exhibited pigs of this type under a succession of breed-names, including Bedfords, Yorkshires, Suffolks, Windsors and combinations thereof. According to my uncle they were almost indistinguishable from year to year. It was felt by sound judges that His Royal Highness was straining after perfection in the German manner, instead of applying the plain, honest principles of his adopted country.

Queen Victoria later exhibited Small White pigs through the agency of her pigman, Nottage. My uncle heard from a friend at Court that Her Majesty toured the sties at Windsor after winning Best Boar at Northampton, though I have not been able to establish what part, if any, she played in the management of the herd.

Royal patronage gave the Small White a vogue among the dilettanti, who were more interested in the call of fashion than in promoting the good name of the English pig. I have heard of instances of these people introducing wooden pillows into the sty, as an added comfort for their reclining favourites. Such antics do no service to the cause of pig-breeding. The serious man has fought shy of a type whose shortness of leg, allied to exceptional bulk, caused it to get under the feet of cattle in the strawyard.

• *The Berkshire* •

It must be a matter of regret to us all that the methods of the late Lord Barrington in laying the foundations of the Berkshire pig were not handed down to posterity. Alas, no record was made before that benefactor departed this life, respected wherever bacon finds favour. The Berkshire is black in colour, but its followers will not countenance a pig without the requisite trace of white on face, feet and tip of the tail. Attempts to get round this stipulation with the aid of a paint-pot have led to scandals in the show ring which I touch on in a later chapter.

The Berkshire has come into its own since the farm labourer became fastidious in his tastes, and demanded a lean cut instead of the fat bacon which had fortified his father. (The discerning Mr Heber Humphrey blamed this

My grandfather knew Barrington. If I had only had the foresight to question him before it too late

on the rise of tinned meats, which I forbid Mrs Whiffle to have in the house.) A debate has since arisen, leading, I regret to say, to acrimony, over an important matter of specification: should the heavy jowl remain a standard point of the Berkshire pig?

The Berkshire

Several members of the Breed Society Committee resigned over the issue after fisticuffs broke out at one of its meetings. The plain fact is that an exaggerated facial contour means a corresponding deficiency in the flank. Since jowl is 7*d.* a pound, and flank is 1*s.* 4*d.*, any breeder in possession of his senses has abandoned the 'Hapsburg' jaw. But the dissenters persist in their folly, calling in aid Lord Barrington, who would have given them the dressing-down of their lives had he still been among us.

That has not been the only bone of contention (if I may so phrase it). Disharmony over the length of the snout has led to further squabbling. If the aim is to produce flitches of length and depth, fine, rounded hams, and well-marbled meat, a longer-snouted animal is essential, and that is an end to the argument. Unfortunately some so-called breeders, who deserve the name of pig-fanciers rather than practical men, wrongly hold that a pug nose denotes high breeding. It is to be hoped that sanity prevails before this methodism drags the proud name of Berkshire in the mud.

Whiffle perhaps a little too emphatic here. Empress's nose to my mind the perfect length

• The Black Dorset •

Space does not allow discussion of the many county breeds with which this country has been blessed. All have their devotees, invariably from the same region as the pig they so admire. The succulence of its pork and the relish of its bacon is defended against all-comers, while a mile across the county boundary the opposite view is expressed with equal force.

The Black Dorset must on no account be confused with the Dorset Black, the original breed of the county. A friend of Mr Frederick Coate, of Sturminster Newton, brought two wild, hairy Turkish sows back to this country, and gave one of them to Mr Coate. He crossed it with a Chinese boar, then crossed the sows of that union with a Neapolitan, and gave the name Black Dorset to the outcome.

It may be asked what, apart from breathing the air, these immigrants had to do with Dorset. The answer is, very little. Mr Coate made belated amends when faced with the problem of in-breeding among his closely-related pigs. He injected a Dorset Black strain into the Black Dorset, to the point where the supremacy of Black Dorset over Dorset Black, or Dorset Black over Black Dorset, became almost impossible to establish. His greatest triumph came at Towcester in 1859, when he defeated the Prince Consort's Windsors, General Bone's Berkshires, Mr Tomb's Whites, and Sir Craster Whiffle's Lincolnshire breed. The Black Dorsets were excellent nurses, but fell from grace when the demand for small, exceptionally fat pigs receded.

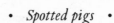

• *Spotted pigs* •

Owners of spotted or 'plum pudding' pigs are as partisan as the champions of the county strains. Once a man has fallen into the way of supporting a certain type, he will swear there is no breed like it. Yet others of us can bear with equanimity whether these piebald pigs keep their spots or change them. Since the white breeds all descend from pigs of darker hue, it stands to reason that the intervening generations will have been parti-coloured. This should be no great cause of wonder, and I must inform the inhabitants of Gloucestershire and indeed any other homes of the spotted pig that I see little virtue in an animal which is a halfway house.

• *The Lincolnshire Curly Coat* •

This is a white pig with an abundant fleecy mantle, designed to withstand the wind off the North Sea which makes our county so bracing. It was brought by my uncle, Sir Craster Whiffle, to a peak of perfection which I feel it my duty to maintain in his memory. Unhappily Sir Craster did not live to see the Lincolnshire Curly Coat recognized with its own class at the Royal.

For many years the authorities feared the intrusion of rival breeds. Never a man to mince his words, Sir Craster made no secret of his view that certain elements were conspiring to see the award of Best In Show go to a small coterie made up of themselves. It was put to him that he would not advance the cause of his chosen pig by blackguarding officialdom. He treated the proposition with scorn, telling me at the time: 'I will see the Lincolnshire Curly Coat in perdition before I become a party to their schemes!' Knowing his attachment to the county breed, I was shocked to hear him contemplate its oblivion, even in the heat of the moment. However, I realized that it signified a deep sense of outrage.

His stand bore fruit, though not in time for him to benefit from it. Spectators at the Royal were thus denied the sight of Sir Craster's famous boar, Silken Pride of Dembleby. My own herd are all descended from this noble sire. When both Sir Craster and his boar had passed beyond the call of competition, those in charge of the pig classes were finally shamed into extending the franchise. The Lincolnshire Curly Coat now takes its rightful place among the finest in the land.

• *The Tamworth* •

The ginger colouring of this breed makes it stand out in company, as do its incorrigible habits. The fence has not been invented which can prevent a Tamworth from getting out and attacking the nearest crop of potatoes. Before the heavier type was introduced it could jump a five-barred gate without difficulty, making it an uneasy neighbour for all except those who had Tamworths of their own, and gave as good as they got.

It is said that one year foreign visitors to Birmingham Show expressed great admiration for the prize-winning Tamworths exhibited by the Lord Mayor. They explained that in their country many farmers lived miles from the nearest market. Such pigs were the only ones which could manage the distance. This is more a commentary on their inferior marketing arrangements than an endorsement of the breed. The restless pig is a thin pig, and the story casts doubt on the claim, which is often heard in Warwickshire, that a Tamworth will grow into a sovereign quicker than any other type.

During some researches into another matter, I chanced on a reference to the Tamworth Manifesto of Sir Robert Peel. Thinking it might refer to the influence of the Corn Laws on the supply of pig feed, I looked into it further, but was disappointed. It merely pledged the Conservative party, against its better judgement I dare say, to accept the Reform Bill of 1832.

• *The Large Black* •

In describing the appearance of this pig I can hardly improve upon its name. Unfortunately size and colour are almost the only features about which its contentious breeders can agree. What started as a minor difference of opinion has blown up into a damaging schism between the eastern and western wings of the Large Black fraternity (to stretch the word to its limits). The East Anglian faction claims the name of Large Black for a well-made pig which goes back to Squire Western's Essex strain. The West Country, on the other hand, holds that its coarser type is the authentic title-holder.

The plain fact is that the Cornish tin-miner is not so particular in his eating habits as the residents of Mayfair and Belgravia, where much of the refined Essex pork is consumed. The friction has now spread to the show ring. It has been said – and with justice – that the awarding of prizes at the Royal has followed 'party lines'. An examination of the records shows a remarkable parallel between the county origins of the judges and those of the prize-winning pigs. For the sake of all that English pig-rearing has stood for, these wreckers must sink their differences and produce a Large Black pig around which regional passions rage no longer.

Following a monograph of mine in the *Lindsey and Kesteven Pig-Breeder* on the colours of the different breeds, I have received these lines from a gentleman in Horncastle:

> The pigmentation of the pig
> Covers many tinges;
> All in their distinctive rig,
> Come blacks and whites and gingers.
>
> Whichever way your fancy leans,
> 'Tis neither fib nor figment,
> That though you know what bacon means,
> You don't know what the pigment.

The tone adopted by my correspondent will grate on the serious reader, but his reasoning cannot be faulted.

VII
A Few Foreign Breeds

THE superiority of our native types of pig is so univer-
sally known that readers may be surprised to find a
chapter on other breeds. However, in a study not only of
the care of the pig, but of its history and dispersal, a
mention of some foreign strains cannot be avoided.

• *The Duroc-Jersey* •

In my travels in the Mid-Western part of the United States
I came upon this breed, known for its thick red coat and
extraordinary constitution. The conditions in which it finds
itself make both a necessity. It is the custom in those parts
to keep the cattle and hogs together. The dietary regime is
one we would deprecate in this country. After feed has
passed through the cattle, the hogs are permitted to supplement their rations by picking over the waste for any
whole grains that have survived the experience. The yard is
often six inches deep in mud, and the temperature well below
freezing. It will be clear why the Duroc-Jersey has been bred
for endurance.

It was put to me in the local vernacular that the farmers
there want 'a hog that will make his own bed, grind his
own corn and wipe his own nose'. They are so scornful of
the Large White, one of the chief glories among our own
breeds, that they condemn it as a 'bandbox hog', a reference

*Shocking way
of proceeding.
Ask Belford
if conditions
improved*

to its supposed delicacy. Since none of the conditions described above apply in this country, the Large White is as
resilient as it needs to be. I shall say no more about the
Duroc-Jersey other than to recommend it be avoided at all
costs.

• *The French Breeds* •

During visits to France I have found the only pigs approaching an acceptable standard are those crossed between English
and native types, notably where the English strain is domi-
nant. A few of the less benighted French are trying to
improve their stock in this way, to little avail. At Birmingham Mr Ainslie Bunch of Naseby boasted he could get
two days hunting a week out of his sow Belle of the Ball, by
selling her pigs to Frenchmen. A single litter, not six months
old, went for fifteen guineas. The French buyers, pinching
and scraping for all they were worth, cried: 'No ginnee! no
ginnee! Ze pound'. However, Mr Bunch, who broke his
neck hunting aged eighty-eight, held out for guineas and got
them. When the bargain was struck his steward, Mr Pipe,
could be seen sketching the fleur-de-lys of France on the
hams of these valuable exports.

French breeders fall into two classes. The peasant proprietor is ill-informed, stubborn, and believes his estate of
four or five acres is the centre of the universe. In contrast,
the educated man has learnt everything out of books and
wants to breed a good pig without stirring from the *salon*.
Their pride and joy is the Craonnaise, which could with
considerable improvement one day stand comparison with
some of the less notable specimens of our own breeds. At
present it is quite inferior.

The pigs of Normandy are furnished with coarse hair, a
thick skin, deficient hams, thin collars and flat sides. They
find favour with the more backward peasantry for one quality, *viz* the ease with which they can be driven to distant
markets. A breeder boasts in *Les Événements de la Société des*

Porcs that French pigs can travel 300 kilometres under their own steam, and asks: 'Could the ponderous English hogs show such endurance?' The answer is no, but since our excellent marketing and distribution system makes such route marches unnecessary, it is no demerit at all.

M. Sainte-Beuve, in his book *Le Porc*, states that French pigs supply meat of the highest quality. His claim is impossible to substantiate because the pork served in France is so smothered in sauces that one might as well be eating rabbit. However, if the lowly specimens I saw were an example of what Sainte-Beuve considers a superior pig, I suggest he crosses the Channel and examines our finest porkers. I have a particular rapport with the French – my ancestor Gaspard Ouiffulhe came over with the Conqueror – and it would give Mrs Whiffle and myself great pleasure to invite him to Longwindley to eat home-killed pork, boiled cabbage and gravy. I am sure he would find it an eye-opener.

One of his compatriots, M. Hallo of Rouen, has already given English breeders the benefit of his views. Said to be a specialist in French methods (a doubtful testimonial), M. Hallo gave a lecture at the Pig-Breeders' Club, which I attended. It was barely five minutes before he had exhausted the patience of his hearers, all of whom, being practical Englishmen, knew more of the subject than he did. M. Hallo's extraordinary mode of address, involving wild gesticulations and interminable pauses for effect (alas, not achieved), his accent, and the absurdity of his opinions made the occasion something of a trial.

Unfortunately it fell to me to offer a vote of thanks to our speaker at the end of this dismal performance. Knowing that the members shared my own views as to the value of what we had heard, I was in a most difficult diplomatic quandary. I decided that as M. Hallo was our guest the tactful approach was my only recourse.

'I am reminded,' I began, 'of the old saying: "to expect little is not to be disappointed". No man of sense, that is to say, no Englishman, would attend a lecture on pig-keeping by an authority from overseas, and expect to have his opinions changed. We are grateful to you, M. Hallo, for confirming us in everything we already knew, even though by the circuitous means of commending the opposite.'

I promised our speaker a list of books by British authors, which would improve his chances of success in the mammoth task he had set himself – that of raising the standards of pig production in his country. In conclusion I drew attention to my Ouiffulhe ancestry, the source of my lifelong warmth towards the French people. This seemed to touch M. Hallo deeply. A flush of gratitude suffused his features and he opened his mouth as if struggling for words. I flatter myself that without in any way suggesting that his audience had enjoyed the experience, my kindly words of encouragement and advice 'sugared the pill', and extricated the club from its predicament.

Sadly M. Hallo was not able to attend the dinner which followed, having remembered a pressing engagement else-where, and he left before I had time to compile the list of English pig books. I sent it on to him, but did not receive an acknowledgement. Doubtless the French are no more fortunate in their postal services than they are in the pig-gery.

· *The Shetland Type* ·

This curiosity is quite distinct from the Old English pig, for which we can be heartily thankful, judging by its descrip-tion. It is said to be the very epitome of a wild boar, yet scarcely larger than a terrier. Its appearance inspired one of the island poets to pen the following lines:

> His bristled back a trench impaled appears,
> And stands erected like a field of spears.

The Shetland pig ranges freely over his demesnes in search of earthworms and roots, excavating pastures and cornfields as he goes. He bivouacks in some potato patch, which he does not leave until he has thoroughly dug it over. The islanders are said to indulge their pig because it is the only one which can withstand the weather. Even allowing for a little poetic licence in the account, most of us would give up bacon for life before letting this brindled monster loose in the neighbourhood.

In most countries men of discernment have imported English stock of the kind already described. There are, however, exceptions. The Pomeranian pig, developed by the Margrave of Bad Oder in the 1840s, grew to an enormous size, but apart from a minor vogue in showing circles never impressed beyond the boundaries of Pomerania. It gained a reputation as a pig that 'did not travel', partly because of its near-immobility, and partly because of a tendency to pine when denied the attentions of the Margrave. When he died, his son, a noted patron of the ballet, showed little interest in the herd. In prize-fighting parlance, the last specimen 'weighed in' at 1,612 lbs and expired near Stettin in 1889.

VIII
Some Pig Breeders of Note

I BEGIN this reminisence of prominent breeders with an account of Lady Bagpurse, who was so attached to her prizewinning pigs that she refused to send them to slaughter. They were permitted to die of old age in magnificently appointed sties, and then buried in a cemetery she had created next to the kitchen garden at Bustable Court, her place in Leicestershire. A gravestone informed visitors of the pig's name and its record in the show ring, together with a short verse composed by Lady Bagpurse. This is how she saluted a favourite Gold Medallist:

> In peace at last, her duty done,
> And every battle honour won;
> A fond companion, and I vow,
> Much more to me than Berkshire sow.

Every year on the day of the Peterborough Show, at which her pigs had carried off so many prizes, Lady Bagpurse would make arrangements for her brother, the Revd Jolyon Stingoe, to conduct a short service at the site. Sprigs of acorns, saved from the previous autumn, were placed on the graves. I have attended this simple ceremony while staying at Bustable Court, and while I deplore undue sentiment, I confess I could scarce withhold a tear as the proud old dowager paid her respects to champions whose day was done.

Most touching. Consider the Empress when time comes at last.

I have less happy memories of the late Sir Everett Slaughter, who inherited a herd of Tamworths from his father and was active in pig circles in the Midlands. He had the habit, disconcerting to those who did not know him, of punctuating his conversation with gunfire, emphasizing important points with a blast from the shotgun he always carried.

The impression of pungent opinions, mingled with the smell of cordite, was not to everyone's taste, and Slaughter made himself thoroughly unpopular with fellow breeders. He was no better liked by his neighbours, particularly when he erected a statue of his boar Behemoth at the main gates of the manor. The faithfulness of the representation caused offence, but a letter from the Parish Council requesting its removal was ignored.

I myself wrote to Slaughter inquiring about the efforts of his late father, Sir Granby, to cross his Tamworth sows with a wild boar. It had been the talk of the Pig-Breeders' Club that the project had run into difficulties (Sir Granby's pigman Heaven was said to have given his employer the choice of retaining either his services, or the boar's). Slaughter's response to my letter not only lacked any filial respect whatever, but was markedly offensive to myself. I ceased the correspondence forthwith.

Slaughter had no heir, but there was a distant cousin, D'Arcy, who pretended to a consuming interest in pigs in the hope of coming into the money. When the will was read, D'Arcy had been left the herd of Tamworths, but everything else had gone to a woman in St John's Wood whom none of Slaughter's acquaintances had ever heard of. D'Arcy sold up and emigrated to Australia. He was hanged after murdering a fellow gold-prospector in Kalgoorlie.

Older readers may recall the furore when the Earl of Clackmannan, hoping to add weight to a speech he was making in defence of the landed interest, let loose a young pig among the Opposition benches in the House of Lords. He had brought it in the Gladstone bag which normally held his reference papers.

Met Slaughter at Shrewsbury one year. Obnoxious fellow. Called my father 'cocky'

The Lord Chancellor suspended the sitting while the messengers attempted to catch the pig, helped by a group of hunting peers, whose blood was roused by the thrill of the chase. It is the habit of animals when pursued to answer the call of nature, in this case causing Lord Dimwood to slip and crack his head on a brass rail. He was carried unconscious from the Chamber, but his friends were later gratified to learn that the wounds were trifling and his mental faculties no worse than before.

The Earl of Clackmannan was censured both by the Government side and his fellow Tories, and was only saved from sterner measures by the private intervention of the Prince of Wales, whose travelling companion he had been on several excursions to Paris. Shunned by his own party, the Earl retired to his estates in Scotland and devoted much time to experimental work in the field of electrical lighting. But his attempt to generate power using gas from rotting pig manure fell foul of public scepticism and insurmountable technical difficulties.

When in India I got to know that great sportsman the Maharajah of Dhownpore. Spunji, as he was known, had two great loves – hunting and cricket. For a time he employed Chuffnell, the Nottinghamshire professional, to bowl to him in the nets every morning. He maintained it got his eye in for pig-sticking in the afternoon.

An inveterate gambler, Spunji kept a herd of Indian jungle swine for racing purposes. Once a year for the Dhownpore Stakes neighbouring princes would bring their fancied runners to compete with his. The pigs would be made ready in traps at the start, while a steaming trough of mash was placed at the other end of the field. Attracted by the aroma, the contestants headed swiftly for the tape, while their supporters urged them on from the sidelines. For ready identification each wore a sash (secured with a clasp of emeralds and rubies) in the colours of its owner; Spunji's, I remember, were gold, purple and sea-green.

Betting was heavy, and Spunji would think nothing of

placing several thousand rupees on a pig. There were no bookmakers, so the wagers were made between individuals. The year his pig Battlecry won the Dhownpore, Spunji's winnings topped the fifty thousand mark – a mere bagatelle to a man in his position.

In the field of scientific experiment none has rivalled Major Madder-Browne, late of the Royal Engineers. He is perhaps best known for his theory – discounted by the Royal Geographical Society – that the Abominable Snowman was a gigantic pig. His inventions created a similar stir, though many were ahead of their time. I think particularly of his steam-driven pig milking-machine, which blew up under testing, demolishing the private laboratory he had built in the grounds of Pottingdean, his house near Camberley.

Madder-Browne had heard that the Chinese regarded sow's milk as highly nutritious, and had served it to unsuspecting sailors and merchants from Europe who called at the port of Canton. He believed there was a market in this country among anaemic girls and so forth, and constructed a device on the suction-pump principle, with multiple teatholders and an automatic back-scratcher to pacify the sow. The machine met with the fate I have described, but I have no doubt that its turn will come.

It was not the mechanics of his sty sluicing system which frustrated Madder-Browne – they worked perfectly; but he could not get the pigs to cooperate. He had let a floor pedal into the part of the sty where dunging took place, and whenever a pig trod on it jet-streams of water were released from pipes above, thus automatically cleansing the fouled area. Pigs are not so foolish as is sometimes supposed, and they rapidly tumbled to the workings of cause and effect. Disliking the cold douche which was the very essence of the system, they learned to avoid the automatic trigger by stepping carefully round it. The last I heard, Madder-Browne was working on a variant involving a network of tripwires.

I am indebted to my uncle, Sir Craster Whiffle, for the following account of the Irish peer Lord Clanbago. He was told it by an eyewitness to the events. One evening Clanbago wagered a dinner-guest that his pig Bluebell would pronounce on the beauty of the view from the roof of the house. It was a fine summer evening, still light enough for the claim to be put to the test, and so the party made its way onto the leads with the pig in train (it was well used to a halter).

The evening sun was casting a glow over the vista of peat-bogs and peasant hovels. However, the pig declined to give voice to any opinion on the subject, and it dawned on Clanbago that he had blown £100 on a very long shot indeed. Never at his best with several hours toping behind him, he reacted by giving the blameless sightseer a kick in the hind-quarters (a man of ungovernable temper, he had been drummed out of the Pig-Breeders' Club for throwing a pork pie at the chef).

So it should have no obstacles in its way, Clanbago had stationed the pig on part of the roof where a section of parapet had fallen off, and never been replaced because of the exigencies of the family fortunes. When his foot landed, the combination of fear and propulsion from behind caused the animal to lunge forward.

The pigman, O'Gormley, who was holding the halter, felt his feet slip under him, and decided that between the fury of his employer and a drop of forty-five feet he preferred the former. As he let go, the pig shot through the gaping parapet and over the edge. With a cry of 'Bluebell!', said to have been heard several miles away, Clanbago rushed forward in time to see his pig dive nose-first into the moat. It had been dug by an ancestor, less from a fear of invasion than from general misanthropy.

As the pig surfaced and began swimming for the opposite bank, Clanbago showed a burst of speed remarkable in a man whose main source of sustenance was alcohol. Bellowing for O'Gormley to follow him, he descended two sets of stairs in a matter of seconds. At the main staircase he reverted to boyhood habits and slid down the banisters, but any advantage was lost as soon as he reached terra firma. Landing on a rug which lay over the polished floor, he slid halfway across the hall before falling with a severely sprained ankle.

As O'Gormley came to the aid of his master, he was greeted with a cry of: 'Never mind me! Save the pig!' Helped by those of the diners still in a condition to do so, O'Gormley hauled Bluebell from the waters, and restored her to the peace and sanity of her sty. Meanwhile the crippled nobleman called for champagne and allowed himself to be helped to a sofa, where he paid over his losses with as good a grace as he could muster.

While waiting for the doctor to arrive with hot and cold compresses, Clanbago recovered his composure by playing backgammon (an incorrigible ne'er-do-well, he later gambled away his inheritance and became a tramp). As my uncle observed, the episode was as good a test as we are likely to have of the old saying: 'If pigs could fly'.

Galahad tells me it was the talk of the Pelican Club that Clanbago was the cause of a murderer being executed by mistake. It was only when he met a party of his tenants returning from the hanging that he remembered he still had the reprieve in his pocket. An incorrigible rotter.

IX
Breeding

NEVER was there a truer word than Sir Craster Whiffle's dictum: 'The boar is half the herd'. The supremacy of the male is an article of faith in the piggery. Compare the influence of two pigs in a herd. One, a sow, endows no more than two litters a year with her vital properties. The other, a boar, bestows his patrimony on dozens.

Thus, in the choice of sire lies the making or breaking of a pig-breeder. Yet time and again on my tours of the country I see a decent herd of sows being put to a specimen which should have been drowned at birth. Slab-sided, thin-shanked and dull-eyed, it scarcely deserves the name of pig, let alone the accolade of boar.

However, even the most able judges can be deceived. I was induced by a scoundrel to buy a prize boar exhibited at one of the principal shows. He seemed a perfectly-shaped animal, and was declared to be out of a sow of my own breeding; but there I was scandalously misled. His introduction to my sows proved disastrous. A latent tendency to 'the blind staggers' (see passage on diseases of the pig) came out in his progeny, and not until his blood had been completely eliminated from the herd did I rid myself of his malign influence.

The marks of a capital boar are a chine that is broad and thick, a level back, wide loins, well-sprung ribs and generous hams. The build should be square, the legs wide apart and the hair fine and silky; coarse hair is often a sign of a villainous temper. He should be of decidedly masculine character, active in his movements, and have fire without ferocity.

Large White boar
'Holywell Windsor'

A boar with undersized testicles, or only one, should be avoided like the plague. As regards the siting of the testicles, there are two schools of thought. Some like to see them protrude immediately below the tail. I cannot agree. They should be set beneath the thickest part of the ham.

Madder-Browne, already referred to, conceived the idea that the scrotal dimensions were a guide to breeding success. I have seen his correlations to the nearest sixteenth of an inch between size and potency. I have neither the time nor inclination to put this pioneering work to the test, but it may present an opportunity for a younger man. Madder-Browne encountered a number of difficulties during his researches, and I can only recommend caution to any who follow his lead.

The features of a fine breeding sow comprise good width throughout, well-sprung ribs giving rotundity, and loins and hams well-filled, with the ham reaching as near as possible to the hock. Nothing is more objectionable in a large-bred pig than a small head. Some judges have been grossly at fault on this point in the show ring; at Norwich one year Sir Craster Whiffle's sow Sylph of Dembleby was beaten by a pig with a head like a pippin. He made his views abundantly plain at the time, and gave these cranks much to think about. At any rate they have been very quiet since.

I have no patience with blushing authors who treat the serving of the sows in such maidenly fashion that the boar might as well not exist. There are instances where the piglets could have arrived through the good offices of the stork, for all we are told about it. I respect the proprieties as much as the next man, but there is no value whatever in these hole-and-corner refinements. Naturally readers would be well-advised not to let the material fall into the wrong hands (servants, young women and so forth), but the subject must be addressed frankly.

As soon as a boar develops a roving eye he should be separated from the herd, or he will start leaping too early. He should be nine months before he commences his duties. If he is allowed to run with the sows he will squander his energies without heed for the morrow by serving the same sow as often as she will entertain him. I cannot emphasize too strongly that an exhausted boar is a useless boar. I recommend that his sty should be well away from the harem, or during periods of heat he will let nothing stand between him and his beloved, often leaving a trail of wreckage behind him.

It is sound practice to keep two boars, one experienced and one 'learning the trade'. As the youngster arrives at a state of potency he should be encouraged to watch his mentor at work. He will pay close attention, and if exceptionally vigorous may need to be discouraged from trying to participate. When his turn comes it is a mistake to introduce him to a skittish young sow, who wishes to play. This will only unsettle the novice. Better that he start his career with a mature pig who has passed this way before, and disdains the role of *coquette*. He should not be overtaxed in the first months of his active life. If he is lukewarm in the company of a consenting sow, give him a week's furlough with a diet of middlings and milk.

A sow in season will show distinct signs of restlessness, but in order to be sure I make a practice of sitting astride her myself. Once the mood is upon her, she might be expected to show a preference for the conjugal boar; but the urge to procreate is so strong that she cares not a fig for the species of her suitor, and signals her readiness for action in unmistakeable fashion.

Now the layman may ask how a creature which cannot speak, and whose range of facial expression is limited, makes her sentiments known. Let me put it in the negative. The human investigator will soon find out if she is not in the frame of mind for dalliance. If he fails to look sharp he will be bundled to the floor with a nip about the flanks for his pains.

That is why I do not recommend this technique to any but an experienced pig-handler. Whenever I adopt it I hold myself in readiness for squalls. At the merest hint of a rebuff I dismount rapidly before she has time to help me on my way. I remember in the early days being made late for church when my sow Winsome retaliated by charging across the sty at full speed. As I fell, by ill luck one leg came to rest in a trough which had recently been filled with slops. From that day I watched carefully for the storm clouds gathering, and made a habit of avoiding the sty before Morning Service. If, however, the sow smiles on my advances it is another matter altogether. I descend in more leisurely fashion and tell my pigman Timbers to take her to the boar at once.

The snout of a boar should not be ringed. It interferes with his sense of smell, and unless his nose tells him what he requires to know he is a broken reed. On the question of

Wellbeloved still reluctant adopt this procedure

mounting, the extent of human intercession will depend on the size and weight of the boar. The block and tackle developed by Madder-Browne can be useful in extreme cases, but Timbers normally finds the assistance of his brother, the village policeman, quite sufficient. It is a far simpler matter to encourage a boar in something he wishes to do than in something he does not.

Unlike many male animals, who discharge their duties in a matter of seconds, the boar is not to be hurried, and may stay in position for twenty minutes. During this time he shows every sign of being lost in thought. The sow, on the other hand, is in full possession of her faculties. She may even wander about the sty while congress is under way, particularly if some titbit in a far corner catches her eye. The boar will trail pensively behind, oblivious to all except the task in hand.

If, with the perversity of the female, the sow spurns the best efforts of the boar, she should be left in his company for twenty-four hours to see if she likes him more on closer acquaintance. His doughty courtship can generally be guaranteed to win acceptance in the end. As to the number of sows he may be expected to serve in a given time, this must vary with the individual. While some could play host to several on consecutive days, to regard this as the norm might leave others jaded.

It will be clear from all I have said that the sty is not a fit place for girls or women during the serving of the sows. No Englishman would countenance such a thing, and it is an unspoken rule that while coupling is taking place female staff should be placed on duties which take them as far from the scene of action as possible.

Some of our old writers made claims for pigs of their acquaintance which take a good deal of swallowing. Both Markham and Mortimer cried up certain sows which gave birth to three litters in a year. Since then some of the cleverest men in England (Sir Craster Whiffle was Senior Wrangler) have looked into the mathematics, and come to the conclusion that Markham and Mortimer were either fools or liars. In other words they either believed the moonshine put about by others, or simply invented it themselves.

In order for this prodigy to be true the sow would be carrying pigs for forty-eight weeks out of the fifty-two. In the four weeks unaccounted for the weary mother would be obliged to suckle two litters and come into heat twice. Much as I relied on my uncle's judgement in such matters, one does not need to have been Senior Wrangler to see that this is beyond any sow that ever lived.

The fecundity of the pig is a mathematical marvel without these flights of fancy. Vauban, Marshal of France in the reign of Louis XIV, dealt with this in his *Mémoires de Statistiques*. He calculated the number of descendants of a single sow over ten generations to be 6,434,838. Vauban allowed only six to a litter, and excluded any offspring of the males, so it is clear the actual number would be far greater. While Vauban is now principally remembered for his inquiries into the prolificacy of pigs, he also invented the ricochet-battery and socket bayonet, and revolutionized the practice of siegecraft.

Some of our English breeders are hopelessly casual in the matter of the herd-book. They expect buyers to accept a pig's pedigree by word of mouth, relying for an approximation of its ancestry on the jumbled memories of the pigman. Even where a herd-book is kept, I recall seeing domestic jottings such as 'tell Mother about Uncle Herbert' scribbled among the bloodlines. I treat all such evidence with misgivings, and avoid any pig which may have undisclosed blots on the escutcheon.

I must say a word about cross-breeding. Much confusion has arisen from the careless use of the term, and it needs to be clarified once and for all. I have been helped in the following definition by Mr Eustace Greathead, the parliamentary draftsman, who has been responsible for the wording of much of our legislation over the past thirty-five years.

I hope his lucid exposition will bring the minutiae within the grasp of the meanest intelligence:

> A cross-bred pig is a pig which has been bred from a dam and sire which have no recorded pedigree, nor pedigree deemed to be capable of registration under breed society rules at the time of classification, or a pig which has been bred indiscriminately from a boar and sow of indeterminate type or breeding, or common pigs of the country, or a pig whose parental ancestry attaches to two different pure breeds, in contradistinction to a pig sired by a pure-bred sow and a common boar, or the contrary, whichever shall apply.

So let there be no more argument about that.

Regret I cannot make head nor tail of this

X
Farrowing and Weaning

WHEN farrowing is imminent the sow will be seen inspecting her quarters with a mouthful of straw and an attitude of the keenest deliberation. From time to time she will deposit bedding in what seems to be her selected nest, and then change her mind and start afresh. If a man at breakfast dithered between one form of egg and another we should not think much of him, but these female caprices in the nursery are of a different stamp. It does not do to question the judgement of the mother-to-be; once a level of intransigence is apparent, the wise man will let well alone.

In India the wild sows show wonderful skill in throwing up a kind of hut made out of sugar cane, with an entrance which they cleverly block when leaving their young. In the farmyard such precautions are unnecessary, but the domestic sow remains a prey to anxiety. Now is the time to ease her qualms, anticipate her wishes, and study her moods.

This requires a meeting of minds which is not given to all of us, though many have remarked on the affinity they detect between myself and the pig species. As to how this comes to be, one might as soon ask how Mozart was able to write the *Moonlight Sonata*. Such things are a gift. Alas, it is not one that is shared by a number of my fellow breeders. Hoping to pacify the agitated sow, they achieve the very opposite.

Blundering novices give themselves much trouble and excitement when they expect additions in the sty. If they

have taken note of the date of service they may rest assured
that a hundred and twelve days later the dam will farrow.
Yet they will have their pigman staying up for a week to
watch her every action, invite half the neighbourhood to
witness the miracle, and communicate such panic to the pig
that she ends by sitting on the litter or, worse still, devour-
ing two or three in her frenzy.

No sow wishes to be introduced to house-party guests or
other strangers at such a moment. Only those whose presence is well known to her should be permitted near the
sty. In my own piggery Timbers and I alone attend the
birth, though when necessary PC Timbers assists.

As regards the happy event, no animal produces her
young so easily as a pig. Being numerous, they are small
enough to negotiate the slipway with none of the adjourn-
ments indulged in by lambs, which are three times the size.
Among pigs the difficulties arise later. Some sows are dainty,
and place their feet and large bodies with infinite
care; others are as clumsy as a carthorse and can scarce
lie down without threatening to suffocate three-quarters
of the litter. Older sows get careless with age, and
are not so attentive when the young complain at being
sat on. Piglets will learn to scatter as soon as the matriarch
looms hazardously above them, but until then they
should be watched closely.

All devotees of the pig must prepare for the role of
midwife to merge with that of undertaker. In the turmoil of
emotion brought on by motherhood, the sow will from time
to time turn cannibal. Very often it is the actions of her
offspring which precipitate the *coup de grâce*. It may seem a
mistake of Nature to furnish the infant pig with teeth. Who
would not pity a sow with fifteen sets of ivories provoking
her when she is not herself? However, in his *Aspects of Pig
Dentition*, Madder-Browne has demonstrated that the teeth
have a useful purpose. They steady the tongue during the
sucking process, allowing it to double over and ·protect the
teat.

*A great
mercy the
Empress has
never shown
this tendency*

Alas, Nature is not infallible. The tongue of one of the new-born may relax its duties. The sow feels a nip and snaps at the offender. Once she has tasted blood the chances of the remaining pigs having a pleasant reception into the world are comparatively slight. Or it may happen that one of the young lets out a squeak in the scramble for a place at the dinner-table. An inexperienced sow, not having learnt that detachment which comes with the years, leaps up in an excess of maternal apprehension. The protective instinct causes her to seize the youngster too eagerly in her mouth, and the story has the same calamitous ending as before.

Markham's remedy was to rub the corpse with the fruit of the stonecrop tree, and present the morsel again to the sow. She fails to notice until too late the nauseating effects of the juice, and is cured of this delinquency for life. Not knowing where I can find a stonecrop tree, I prefer to partition her off with a hurdle in the sty, so each piglet can be laid away from her. After the last is born she may be calmer and receive them with the tenderness we would expect. In the case of a persistent offender there is no choice but to convert her into bacon at the earliest opportunity.

When these horrors can be avoided, no animal is more solicitous of her young. It is most affecting to see the little creatures make their way to the head of the prostrate parent, and appear to soothe her after the night's exertions. She, with many a dulcet grunt and wheeze, assures them of the boundlessness of mother-love.

As little as possible of the bedding should be replaced with fresh straw. If the nest is disturbed the house-proud mother will give all her attention to rebuilding it, leaving the piglets cold and forgotten. Worse still, some may become concealed in the restoration work and meet an untimely fate when she decides to lie down again.

After farrowing, the sow will be off her food for as long as two days, but may be tempted by an appetizer of warm treacle. Then she will take a thin slop of sharps, fortified by a little rough cider as a pick-me-up. It may be necessary at this delicate time to dress her with an emollient. A mixture of Gallipoli oil and carbolic acid in a proportion of eight to one will bring relief. For constipation a dose of linseed tea is often a great boon, but in obstinate cases there is no finer recourse than Epsom salts in soapsuds. A pinch of ginger may be added for good measure.

Peace would reign among the little mess-mates were it not for a mystery of nature: the flow of milk varies between one teat and another. When the piglets find those at the front of the sow a richer source of supply than those towards the rear, the ructions begin.

Once it is up and running, a small pig's first concern is to outrank its siblings and the devil take the hindmost. It therefore spends much of its waking moments pressing for advantage. The sow is often at her slumbers while the feuding rages, and dispenses largesse without favour; but her offspring do not rest till they settle the order of precedence. Thus, in a line of sucking pigs you may always see the lustiest at one end, and the runt at the other.

Further quarrels may be expected if young from a different litter are introduced. It would be mighty convenient if a sow with teats to spare could only extend her hospitality to the overflow from another sty; but the cussedness of the pig makes this no easy matter.

It is not the sow who is the troublemaker. Except when visiting the trough she is almost permanently at rest, and may raise no objection to the pirating of her supplies. The little pigs are not so accommodating. Since every litter has a fragrance it regards as its own, their snouts tell them when there are strangers in their midst. They turn on the intruders, nip their tails and deny them access to the udder.

A way of outfoxing the infant chauvinists is to smear them with a little paraffin. This blots out the family trademark and gets them accustomed to a new one. It is then a simple matter to give the trespassers a similar coating. The warring parties can no longer tell each other apart and can be re-introduced with every prospect of peace. Contrary to

Get
Wellbeloved
onto this

the claims of rogues at village fairs, pigs cannot count, so the rise in population passes unnoticed.

Madder-Browne devised another method, which failed to catch on beyond the boundaries of his own piggery. He stationed a boy, at 6d. a day, to stand guard over the alien pigs armed with a pea-shooter. Each time a newcomer was elbowed off the teat by one of the incumbents, the young sniper aimed a riposte at the rear of the culprit.

Pigs are remarkably quick to learn where their best interests lie. They soon found that any devilment was followed by a smarting reminder from a dried pea, and acquired better manners. Madder-Browne told me that all worked well as long as one could maintain the vigilance of the sentry; but he was not the first to discover that a boy's attention will wander. Once the joys of marksmanship had begun to wear thin, day-dreaming and then truancy generally followed.

After a month the piglets will want to share their mother's food. At first they may content themselves with titbits that go flying as she bolts her rations. Later they will invade the trough, chancing a nip from her cavernous jaws, and should then be supplied with their own dish of sharps with a little whole milk; separated milk is apt to be constipating. As a further preventive I get Timbers, before retiring, to disturb the pigs from their nest. Being by nature the cleanest of animals, they will not foul where they lie, and in the darkness they may go too long without a motion. A short promenade of the sty in the late hours encourages regular habits.

When the day comes for the young to leave home, the broken hearts are all on one side. The sow is by now weary of them and glad of the rest. They, however, believe fleetingly that the world has come to an end, and set up an almighty complaint until they find something that diverts them.

If they are left a little hungry on the morning of parting, they can readily be tempted from the sty with a bucket of

refreshments. The sow will watch them go with quiet satisfaction, and they have reached their new quarters before
they realize anything is amiss. The ensuing lamentation,
though vigorous, soon gives way to the unmistakeable sound
of a dozen pigs banqueting on sharps and boiled potatoes.

XI
Rearing and Keeping

I HAVE known grown men approach the business of gelding like so many young ladies frightened at a mouse. They will turn their hands to minor surgery of other kinds with gusto; yet faced with castrating the young boars, they grow pale. These faint-hearts have no option but to call in the village 'cutter'. Often an old labourer or blacksmith no longer able to do heavy work, he tours the farms for miles around offering his services at a shilling a litter.

Yet in truth any owner or stockman could do the job himself after a little study. I deplore the custom, still known in certain parts, of using the teeth as pincers after the incision has been made. It is somewhat coarse, and un-hygienic to boot. For the preferred method I recommend a reading of Madder-Browne's 'Notes on the History and Practice of Castration' (*Lindsey and Kesteven Pig-Breeder* vol. XCII, No. 5), which deals with the matter in exhaustive detail. Few pigs suffer ill effects after the initial un-pleasantness, especially if a little goose oil is applied with a feather.

It is advisable to spay those gilts, or young females, which are not to be used for breeding (if they are left to come in heat they make less weight, and become a nuisance by mounting their companions). This is a more complicated manoeuvre than gelding, and requires the attendance of a veterinarian. One such, Mr Jevons Barmistead of Melton Mowbray, went down in the annals of his profession for a feat of spaying that was never equalled before or since. He undertook for a wager to spay a hundred gilts in two hundred minutes.

That number being procured, and umpires appointed from among neighbouring practitioners, Mr Barmistead commenced operations at 10 a.m. in the Pie and Potboy at Melton, where the bet had been made. The first eleven took only twelve minutes. Mr Barmistead required fifty-nine-and-a-half minutes to dispose of another forty-five, keeping victory well within his sights, and shortening the odds to ten to one on. Yet such was the sporting fervour of the crowd that bets were coming in as fast as they could be laid.

However, Mr Barmistead gave his backers some anxiety when he began to slow markedly owing to fatigue. There was deeper concern when pig number eighty-one detained him for seven-and-a-half minutes, owing to malformation of the vitals. At that point the odds drifted out to evens and no takers. Happily Mr Barmistead found a second wind as he neared his century, and despatched the ninety-third in fifty-six seconds. He completed his task within eight minutes and forty seconds of the given time, to the delight of his admirers. All except the bookmakers stayed to celebrate his triumph. The above account was supplied to me by Mr Percy Thimbell, whose father, Noah, was landlord of the Pie and Potboy and timekeeper for the occasion.

I now turn to a matter Sir Craster Whiffle often spoke of as the Alpha and Omega of pig-keeping – the sty. In his book *Le Porc* Sainte-Beuve condemns French piggeries as draughty, damp and wretchedly kept. In my experience he has, if anything, understated the case. However, I have not the satisfaction of thinking our own are much better. In this deficiency we keep company with the French.

Once, while inspecting a primitive sty a yard deep in manure, I was assured by the farmer of its great practical value. I questioned the confounded fellow further and was told that the soft cushion beneath the nest yielded to pressure when the dam turned over, thus saving her pigs

Galahad knew people who attended this event. One a member of the Pelican.

from a flattening. I spent some hours explaining to him the details of Madder-Browne's patent piggery, with its two-decker sties, but ignorance on such a scale is beyond salvation.

How a country admired throughout the world for the quality of its swine tolerates these conditions is a mystery to all right-thinking people (I may say the apathy extends to the Editor of *The Times*, who has failed to publish several letters of mine on the subject). By blaming the state of the sty on the occupant, the culprits add slander to their other misdemeanours. As so often, Sir Craster Whiffle put the matter in a nutshell. 'A pig is as clean as his master', he would reply stiffly, when these backsliders made their excuses.

Under the Madder-Browne system, which I have adopted at Longwindley, the sleeping quarters are above ground. Visitors are surprised to see how nonchalantly the most ponderous sow will mount a ramp (strutted so she does not miss her footing) to reach the upper storey. She may be suspicious at first, but is easily won over with the use of sugared bon-bons.

If these are placed at intervals along the ramp, all anxieties will be put to one side. The sow will ascend with thought only for her favourite comfits, the last few located within the bed-chamber itself. Not until they are despatched will the new tenant show the slightest interest in her surroundings. Then, having found the accommodation to her liking, she will normally take a well-earned rest. Should she seem reluctant to return to ground level, a further trail of sweetmeats will soon change her mind. Thereafter the journey will lose its fears, and she will retire upstairs as stately as a duchess. So discriminating is she that she will keep the dormitory spotlessly clean, saving her natural functions for the yard below.

In earlier days Timbers and the backhouse boy would load the muck-cart on the third Saturday of each month, to the accompaniment of much moping and grumbling. How-

Try similar for Empress? Ask at Shrewsbury

ever, Madder-Browne provides for a hole to be made in the front wall of each sty; this enables Timbers to sluice the droppings into the sewer. The pipes run below ground straight into the muck-cart, which stands in its own dug-out with sloping access. Hauling a cart full of dung up the gradient proved too much for the horses, but the traction engine I obtained from Gormandroyd and Crump of Hunslet makes light work of it.

Sometimes a pig will put the whole system in peril by bedding down in the yard and relieving herself up above. She will even bring mouthfuls of straw from her erstwhile nesting place to make herself more comfortable below. Madder-Brown has anticipated this irregularity, and recommends a scattering of half-bricks round the yard. No pig likes to feel fragments of builders' rubble amidships, and she soon hastens aloft for a less fretful doze.

It is often forgotten that the late Mr Herbert Treadgold, the architect, was also a distinguished pig-breeder. His herd enjoyed perhaps the most lavish quarters of any in the country. Treadgold was accustomed to thinking on the grand scale. He created a sensation in 1868 with his plans for an enormous railway terminus in Hyde Park, which were abandoned after the personal intervention of Queen Victoria (the incident was said to have cost Treadgold a knight-hood).

Disappointed in his ambitions, he turned his attention to pig-sties of equally grand design. Marble pillars, classical friezes and many-chambered luxury were the hallmarks of these dwellings, which I saw on a visit to Treadgold at his home near Stow-on-the-Wold. He had become increasingly eccentric, and would often take his meals in the sty at the same time as the pigs. I remember him complaining of the problem he had in keeping staff, once they discovered this aspect of their duties. In later years Treadgold devoted as much time to his herd as rest cures at an establishment specializing in his type of case would allow.

Catching a pig is fraught with difficulty for the novice. It knows that disagreeable consequences can be expected, and exerts itself mightily to avoid them. A sow possesses a punitive set of teeth and does not hesitate to sink them in the object of her wrath. A boar is even better-armed, and worse-tempered into the bargain; anyone interfering with his liberties can be certain of reprisals. I use the 'Hangman's Pig-Catcher' invented by Madder-Browne, but beginners should on no account put it to the test until they have taken instruction.

The device is a clever variant of the carrot-and-stick principle. It gets its name from the noose which plays an important part in the capture. Both noose and carrot are suspended in the correct juxtaposition from the end of the stick. When the carrot is presented to the animal it clamps its teeth eagerly over the tit-bit, and its upper jaw is introduced willy-nilly into the noose. That is the moment to tighten the cord and secure your pig to the nearest post.

Empress so amenable hangman quite unnecessary

As a warning to the unwary I should mention the misfortune which befell Timbers, when first using the 'hangman'. He contrived to over-extend the noose to such a degree that it reached the ground. Not realizing that he had one foot inside the trailing loop, he followed the tightening procedure only to find himself sent flying as the indignant pig made off. This experience was most beneficial in persuading Timbers to pay greater attention to what he was doing.

The 'hangman' will perform the work of three when a pig that is off-colour baulks at taking his medicine. Finding the cord irksome, he opens and closes his mouth in an effort to be rid of it. Now is the time to be ready with an old shoe, which has had the toe cut off. At a moment when the jaws are fully open the attendant will thrust the shoe into the aperture, taking care to remove his hand before they snap shut again. The pig's interest will be captured by the arrival of something he can get his teeth into. Before the shoe disappears altogether the attendant should pour the medicine into it. Without the pig realizing, the beneficial fluid finds its way through the hole at the toe and down his throat.

This is an improvement on the old method, in which several men would be called on, first to catch the pig and then to hold it. Finally, with a can similar to that used for oiling machinery, one of them would squirt the specific into each nostril in turn. The pig does not understand that this may be a life-saving operation, and protests violently. With the 'hangman' and shoe, on the other hand, one fellow can make short work of the whole business.

In the old days when anything went wrong, the farmer would send for the 'pig-doctor'. That worthy's pretensions to leechcraft rested on some antiquated recipe, used as a panacea for all ills. Very often it would have been handed down by an ancestor famous for real or imagined cures. The unfortunate pig would be dosed with this liquor, consisting of whatever abominations happened to be at hand.

After some learned clinical remarks to the bystanders, and a mug of beer, the 'doctor' would leave his patient to contend with both the disease and the remedy. One or other normally brought the case to a rapid conclusion, except when the obstinacy of the pig caused it to live on in spite of both.

My uncle told me of an instance near Sleaford when one of these practitioners was called in. He diagnosed 'a bit of a cold' and gave the pig some warm water, promising to make up a bottle of cure-all and bring it in the evening. So invigorating were the effects of the water that the pig was soon running about as briskly as ever in life. Come the evening the medical man arrived and forcibly administered the maximum dose, charging 1s. 2d. for the privilege. The following morning the pig was found dead, as clear a case of the cure being more fatal than the disease as you could wish to hear of.

A clue to the ingredients of these deadly potions may be found in Gervase Markham's *Cheap and Good Husbandry*. For murren or plague he recommends a warm solution of hen's dung and boiled liverwort. Measles in swine, claims Markham, will respond to red ochre and whey, mixed with the oldest urine that can be found. It is a tribute to the gameness of the pig that some of them presumably survived these ministrations.

For pox Markham would have us annoint the sores with brimstone and boar's grease, which had the virtue of probably not being fatal. The same cannot be said for his suggestion in cases of the sleeping evil – a dosing with juice of the stonecrop fruit. It will be remembered from Chapter X that he urged the use of this emetic to discourage cannibalism in sows. Anything more guaranteed to finish off an indisposed pig even Markham has not given us.

A later author, Loudon, rejects these kill-or-cure measures. Instead he advocates a hearty meal, come what may. Diseases as varied as the staggers, quinsy and heavings (inflammation of the lungs) will all, he advises, improve with pease and pollard, washed down with a cordial of treacle and strong ale. Any pig prepared to do justice to such a treatment is a pig which is not very ill in the first place.

In this regard, as in so many others, the pig population owes much to the wisdom of Sir Craster Whiffle. He made an extensive study of country and scientific remedies and published his findings in the *Lindsey and Kesteven Pig-Breeder*. Sir Craster was able to demonstrate which specific is likely to accelerate the decline, and which may put life into a sick pig. The following are among those that received his imprimatur.

The strangles, or quinsy: A dosing with ipecacuanha, white hellebore and tartar. Cover the head and neck, and place a vessel of hot water and smartweed under the snout of the pig. The steaming inhalations will penetrate the air pipes and bring relief.

Wild fire (gangrenous erysipelas): A purgative of Epsom salts in soapsuds will often clear the trouble.

The scours: For piglets, a little soot in the feed, and a teaspoon of alum water twice a day. In adults chalk and a dose of kermes (trisulphide of antimony) will moderate an over-active bowel.

The blind staggers: Causes the pig to gyrate, nearly always in the same direction. Pour melted lard or castor oil into one of the ears, preferably that towards which the pig turns. Another remedy is a sharp blow in the middle of the fore-head.

Inflammation of the teats: Subject the sow to a cooling regime, and dress the parts with lotions of linseed and marsh mallow.

Inversion of the anus: Apply a little laudanum to the affected region and push it back whence it came.

Lice: Rub in a mixture of one part lard to two parts kero-sene.

Mange: Apply a mixture of one part creosote to forty parts lard oil. Spratt's Dog Soap may do just as well.

Red soldier or black jack (swine fever): Give drinks of but-termilk, and place a blister of turps and mustard on the belly.

With the aid of these tried and trusted restoratives pigs at Longwindley have been brought back to full vigour after few would have bet twopence on their chances.

This treatment a great blessing for the Empress just before Shropshire Show one year

I have found the vets lamentably unresponsive on the few occasions when the Empress has been off her food. Happily her appetite fully restored soon afterwards

XII
Feeding

A PIG'S stomach is one of the wonders of nature. Sainte-Beuve devoted a chapter of his *Le Porc* (trans. Tibbalds) to a detailed study of its functions. He dealt at length with the glandular structure, the pyramidal appendix, and the villous mucous membrane. Suffice it to say that when in working order these organs can absorb an abundance of eatables which in any other animal would bring the digestive system to a standstill.

Sainte-Beuve measured the alimentary canals of one hundred and eighty-five pigs, and found the average length fell a few inches short of that of a cricket pitch.* Fellow omnivores cannot match the extent and proficiency of this tract. It allows the pig to gulp its food in a way that has caused adverse comment only among those who have made no attempt to understand pig morphology.

Because a human cannot do the same without dyspepsia, the ill-informed would have us believe that the pig is *ipso facto* a glutton. On the contrary, it is no more eager to experience dyspepsia than are blinkered critics, but it knows its capacities better than they do. There are circumstances in which it will show a refinement of taste which might surprise these imbeciles. The peach growers of North America run pigs in their orchards, and let them feast on the copious windfalls. The fortunate epicures reject the peaches which dropped but a short time before, and watch intently for a fresh fall.

* So far as I know, Sainte-Beuve was not familiar with cricket. He employed the metric system, and Tibbalds followed suit, but this is no earthly use to any but continental readers. To make the thing intelligible, it is I who have introduced the sporting illustration.

Such is the constitution of this indomitable feeder that it will eat till it can scarcely stand, and after a suitable respite come back for more. Naturally I refer to a diet based on wholesome ingredients. Even a pig's intestines will mutiny if presented with the garbage which passes for nourishment in some quarters.

Loudon comments that if allowed to roam upon the dunghill, pigs will forage for unbroken grain that has passed through the horses. I concede that they are indiscriminate in their tastes, and this encourages fools to give them nothing but the scrapings and leavings from house and yard. The 'hog-cistern' still lingers in certain districts as a repository for every kind of offal. As Sir Craster Whiffle used to say of such cases: 'A neglected pig saves his complaints for the dinner-table'.

It is a little-known fact that the late Count Tolstoy, the progressive landlord who was also a novelist in his spare time, suffered great inconvenience while superintending the feeding of pigs. They ate several hundred pages in manuscript of a book of his called *War and Peace*, in the village of Bogorodovsk. I was told this by my cousin Ernest Whiffle, who was First Secretary at our embassy in Moscow. He had learned of it from Tolstoy's land agent, whom he had met through a shared interest in the poet Burns.

It was the Count's habit, while touring his estate, to fill in the time by jotting down the light fiction for which he had discovered a talent (in an active life I have not had the opportunity to read any of his works, though I believe they are quite amusing). Once, while visiting an outlying farm, Count Tolstoy was inspecting an hydraulic-powered swill-mixer of his own design, and had placed his manuscript on a ledge near the machine.

He had overlooked the fact that the mechanism caused a lever to swing across the space where his notebooks lay. While the attention of the party was concentrated on the swill-bin in front of them, the documents were swept un-noticed into the grinder at the rear. By the time they came into view they had been shredded, pulped, mixed with bran mash and rendered unrecognizable.

The pigs had been waiting impatiently by a trough near the mouth of the mixer, and it was not until they had eaten their fill that the Count realized his loss. He had years of farm visiting in front of him in which to repair the damage, but I understand that he never felt the published version was quite as good as the original.

Sir Craster Whiffle, a lifelong bachelor, cared more for his pigs than many a family man for his own flesh and blood. He had a wonderful eye for a champion, and used to select his show animals at an early age. He would bring them on with a diet of meal, currants and milk, rolled into balls the size of an egg.

Such was the interest in Sir Craster's herd of Lincolnshire Curly Coats that he had visitors daily, and their great delight was to watch him feed his young prodigies. In one hand he held a jug of cream, into which he dipped the bun before proffering it to one of the pigs. After a few trials they would sit up to be fed like any young chit in the nursery. As a result of regular handling his prize-winners always behaved impeccably in the show ring.

Since an honest day's work has gone out of fashion, the man with a substantial herd has had to invest in new-fangled feeding equipment. There was a time when the attendant visited every sty with a bucket. Now the pigs can whistle for their dinners unless he has every provision of the modern age. If the pigman can be prevailed upon to push it, the food carriage made by Peabody and Fawcett of Dudley answers the purpose at a modest outlay. It rotates on a wheeled axis, so that the mash or swill can be tipped conveniently into the trough.

Since Timbers has been complaining of lumbago I have had to go a stage further and have a tramway installed by Gormandroyd and Crump of Hunslet. By this means a truck can be run the length of the piggery with the greatest possible convenience. The feed issues from a chute on either

I did not like to say so to Galahad but it was just as well the Empress ate his reminiscences. Connie would have been quite impossible if they had been published

side, and the speed of the operation means that it reaches the pigs in a hotter and fresher state than before. Timbers is a man of few words except when nursing a grievance. I interpret his recent silence on the subject of lumbago as signifying hearty approbation of the new arrangement.

At the tramway terminus stands the boiler for the steaming of roots, meal and corn, and for heating the swill. The model I have from Truelove and Thripp of Peterborough will cook potatoes at a cost in fuel of a farthing a hundredweight. I insist that only the finest ingredients are used at Longwindley. When Timbers has the early-morning feed bubbling away in the boiler, the aroma of bran mash or barley meal and potatoes quite sharpens my appetite for breakfast.

The young boars should be separated from the litter soon after weaning or they will jostle the sows off their food. Pigs are such feverish eaters that if one or two fail to get their snouts in the trough in the first minute they may end with nothing at all. There is a tendency in the mêlée for the swill or mash to fly everywhere. Madder-Browne has overcome this problem with his Patent Non-spill Trough. Its principle feature is an adjustable flange, which allows a pig with a prominent chap to eat with the same delicacy and comfort as one that can dip into a quart pot.

Breeders within range of London obtain splendid results by feeding their pigs on hotel waste. It can be bought for next to nothing in a solid, jelly-like form known as Tottenham Pudding, and should be mixed with bran to give it body. It is all the same to a pig whether his meals come from Claridges or the adjoining field, but the leftovers of well-to-do diners add exceptional calorific value. The pigs show great finesse in sifting through the knives, razor-blades, broken glass, etc. which find their way into the pudding. Any attempt to stop them approaching the trough like a rugger scrum intent on scoring is quite futile. Yet they emerge without a scratch.

Since the outbreak of hostilities in Europe, shortages have

forced breeders to seek new sources of feed. Sustaining the
supply of bacon is essential if the Kaiser is to receive a
trouncing, and victuals should on no account be wasted.
The inhabitants of many towns are encouraged to place
their refuse in bins marked 'eatables' and 'uneatables'. In
Market Harborough they have been inspired by the patriotic
rallying-cry: 'British pigs versus German swine'.

On my travels in the Orient I came across a method of
feeding household waste to livestock which beats everything
for ease and efficiency. Unfortunately it would not do in this
country, since you could never persuade an Englishman to
put his house on stilts. In parts of the East which are
plagued by flood and earthquake there is no choice in the
matter. They do so or perish.

However, they make a virtue of their troubles by keeping
the family pig in the space below the house. A trap-door is
let into the floor and kitchen scraps and other unmention-
ables tossed through to the waiting pig below. I cannot say
the animals I saw were top-notchers (the nearest equivalent
would be a middling specimen in France), but I have no
doubt they keep body and soul together in these households
of a dozen half-starved Orientals.

Like human beings, whom they resemble in so many
ways, pigs enjoy a little variety from time to time. A new
sty, a new paddock (though they are suspicious of new
company) lend interest to a life which may otherwise slip
into a rut. For this reason, in the autumn I send the village
children into the woods to glean acorns for the herd at a
halfpenny a sack. Thus throughout the winter, when cold
and damp keep them in, I am able to brighten the day by
distributing a *bonne-bouche*, to which every pig looks forward
with the keenest interest.

Since they are creatures of habit, at three o'clock every
afternoon, whatever I am doing, I make a point of breaking
off and heading for the piggery. I am greeted by a scene of
the liveliest animation; they know to the minute at what
time I can be expected. The most majestic sow, mother to

dozens, skips round her sty like a spring lamb in anticipation of the treats to come.

After the largesse, I sometimes help Timbers with grooming. Sir Craster Whiffle maintained that this operation is worth a double ration of feed. Brushing the coat and then rubbing in a little light oil prevents annoyance from vermin and promotes a feeling of contentment in pigs of every kind. It aids the incorporation of their last meal, and acts as a stimulating prelude to their next.

A well fed boar of the Essex strain

XIII
A Day at
Longwindley

I AM woken at seven by Pounce with a glass of hot water and a Lardy John (the latter is made from flour, currants and rendered lard to an old Lincolnshire recipe, which I detail in full in the chapter on the culinary aspects of the pig). I find this combination gives the digestive system its 'marching orders'.

By the time I have consumed the above Pounce has run the bath, and after my ablutions in no time I am eagerly crossing the yard in the direction of the sties. My arrival is timed to coincide with the feeding of the herd, via the steam-driven tramway which runs the length of the piggery. Timbers has been up for some hours, firing the engine and loading the feed-mixer with bran mash etc.

As described earlier, the system delivers its load by tipping the speciality of the day into the troughs along its path. Timbers and I then walk past each sty noting the reaction of the occupants to the arrival of food. In the normal pig, it is one of enthusiasm bordering on hysteria; anything short of this is a sure sign of seediness.

It does not require a veterinarian to work out that a pig which greets the arrival of breakfast with a fit of the sulks is not itself. Banting is a clear reversal of all we expect of the species. Timbers and I decide whether to call in the sawbones, or whether one of the specifics in his medicine chest is all that will be necessary. By this time I find that the hearty appetite of those pigs which are in rude health

Tell Connie
Baxter quite
mad and
must go
Insist

has communicated itself to the human animal, and I hasten back to the house.

Under the direction of Mrs Whiffle, Cook prepares for me a breakfast of eggs, bacon, pork sausages and savouries such as pig's fry or brain fritters. Very often after breakfast I have a visit from students of the pig who arrive from various parts of the Empire and beyond to study my methods. Whenever possible I arrange for a dozen or so to come in one party, and I have had to adopt my own methods of communication. There is no time to ascertain that Mr Wah Hei from Penang or Mr Gruentz from Budapest – I choose two names at random from a party I have received this morning – is following every word.

Sometimes I am obliged to take refuge in sign language and the kind of gesticulation so beloved of continentals, but otherwise plain spoken English has to do, whether they like it or not. Mrs Whiffle tells me I have a carrying voice; occasionally it has been the cause of contention between us. However, it is a great blessing when I need to speak to anyone in my employ who happens to be a couple of fields away.

My father was similarly gifted

I find it easier to communicate with foreigners when I raise the volume to the level one might use while standing, shall we say, near a military band. They seem to have a better grasp of what is being said, at any rate if the tailing-off of jabbering interruptions is anything to go by. Trial as it is dealing with these people, I feel it a duty to show them what has made the name of English pig-breeder the desideratum it has become.

My other contribution to 'spreading the gospel' has been to allow a small number of young people to come and work on the estate for a period of six months or so. Their families pay a suitable premium, plus a modicum for board and lodging. I house them in the lofts above the stable-block, which can accommodate a dozen or so in the simple dormitory I have provided. They have unlimited access to the cold tap in the yard and are permitted to undertake all the heavier work for which youth and inexperience equip them.

At least once a week I make a point of setting aside half-an-hour or so in order to instruct them in the basics of pig-rearing. Of course that is by no means their only opportunity to benefit from their stay at Longwindley. By helping Timbers muck out the sties, load the swill-mixer and so forth, they gain invaluable experience for the future.

The gratitude of these youngsters is a joy to behold. They may not say much during their time here, though any signs of sullenness are merely the result of absorption in their tasks, and a healthy state of fatigue once they are completed. However, there is no mistaking the distant chatter that emanates from their quarters on the day of departure. If I am any judge of young blood, they are swapping tales of a time well spent.

As I bid them farewell, it almost seems as if they can hardly wait to leave, so eager are they to put into practice all I have taught them. They often indicate in so many words that their six months here are an experience they will never be able to forget, and promise one day to repay me for the treatment they have received; but to see these lads go off to become the pig-breeders of the future is reward enough. I ask no more.

During the latter part of the morning I attend to the correspondence which pours in from all parts of the globe. Only today I had a letter from a Welsh émigré in Patagonia, asking which breed of pig was most suitable for the damp and chilly climes to which he had exiled himself. He evidently misses the bacon and laver bread to which he had grown attached in his native Wales.

I wrote back suggesting he should either return home or stick to sheep, enclosing the small invoice I think reasonable when my advice is sought. Regrettably not all my correspondents see fit to honour their debts. I get my secretary Miss Tumbrill to make a list of these levanters, so that if they have the impudence to solicit my opinion again I can be sure to disappoint them.

By this time the sound of Pounce ringing the gong tells me it is time for luncheon. Mrs Whiffle arranges a simple repast of thick broth, perhaps some spare ribs or belly of pork with dumplings, followed by steamed pudding and then cheese and biscuits. People often ask me if I do not tire of my diet. The answer is no. I explain that when eating in the houses of other people I am obliged to take pot-luck, though most of my circle of acquaintances keep pigs and share my tastes. Then on Christmas Day Mrs Whiffle likes to serve turkey, and I fall in with her wishes; but the emphasis at Longwindley is on the pig, at the dinner-table as elsewhere. The force of my remarks is such that the interrogator rarely pursues this line of inquiry.

After luncheon I revisit the piggery, paying particular attention to the work of the boars. First I conduct trial mountings with any likely candidates among the sows (as described earlier), and then superintend the serving of those which respond in the affirmative. Next I tour part of the estate on my horse Nigger, before joining Mrs Whiffle and any company she may have for tea of sandwiches, scones, cakes and so forth.

It is then time to retire to my study, where Miss Tumbrill takes down at my dictation lecture notes and articles, including the column I contribute to the *Lindsey and Kesteven Pig-Breeder* in succession to my late uncle. In order to give Miss Tumbrill more interest in her work, I have suggested she should join me on my early-morning tour of the sties and acquire some knowledge of herd management. She thoroughly approves the plan, but tells me she has never been able to go near pigs on the grounds that they make her sneeze. One can only admire the philosophical way she endures her handicap.

A final sortie to the yard is required to check that all is well among my sleeping beauties. I was as fond a parent as the next man when the children were in the nursery, and felt a burst of paternal sentiment when I visited the little devils in their cots; but I confess that at the twilight hour a

Whiffle very clever expressing what we all feel

snoring sow with a litter of ten produces in me a not dissimilar emotion. For the pig devotee there is no sight quite like it.

Tearing myself away with difficulty, I race through the preliminaries if I am to avoid censure from Mrs Whiffle for arriving late in the drawing room before dinner. If we have guests, which is very often the case, we delight in giving them a succulent roast of home-killed pork. After we have eaten, the ladies retire to play écarté for a small stake. This allows the gentlemen to give fuller attention to pig matters than was possible in the chit-chat over dinner (it is a vagary of the female sex that pigs are not a fit topic of conversation in mixed company).

Having parleyed at length over the port, we rejoin the ladies briefly until the party goes its separate ways. Mrs Whiffle and I then spare a moment before we retire, for a resumé of events and the laying of plans for the morrow. Such is the pattern of life at Longwindley. After the regulation eight hours I awake next day ready to extend the common stock of pig knowledge yet further.

Whiffle knighthood? Make representations

XIV
The Cottage Pig

SIR CRASTER WHIFFLE did more for the cottage pig than any man in England. He expressed his philosophy thus in the *Lindsey and Kesteven Pig-Breeder*: 'The grunting of a hog in a cottager's sty sounds sweeter than the song of the nightingale. There is no finer ornament for the cottage wall than a side of bacon'.

Sir Craster built model cottages for all his men, each with a sty in the back garden, and was tireless in instilling the principles of pig-keeping among the humbler classes. For the better type of labourer, a pig is companion, helpmeet and savings bank. It stops him squandering his earnings on beer and baccy, and keeps his family through the winter.

William Cobbett was a Radical, but from time to time he spoke sense. I am heartily with him when he says that a man who cannot live on solid fat bacon wants the sweet sauce of labour. The number of such milksops is growing by the day, owing to the decadence of the age. However, a few pence a week on meal is a sound investment for the fellow who lives by the sweat of his brow. He can feed his pig up to twenty-five score by All Saints' Day, sell a ham, put the money towards a successor, and keep the rest for family consumption at barely any cost to himself.

The more enterprising man may even aspire to a little farm of his own. Mr Roley Budge, the celebrated breeder, started as stockman for Mr Colenso Knyvett at Much Wenlock, and saved ten shillings to buy his first gilt. Summer feed cost him next to nothing. The larger householders in the district granted him the use of their kitchen scraps, and in the winter he spent a portion of his wages on meal. His employer permitted him to cut coarse herbage from the hedges and ditches, which he buried in a silo pit for winter use. His eight children were sent gleaning in the woods for acorns and beech mast, and his sow Pearl came on so well she was soon the object of admiration for miles around.

The services of Mr Knyvett's boar resulted in a first litter the following March. Budge sold a few pigs at a good price, and fattened the remainder on the proceeds. He kept the best gilt as a second sow, and repeated the process as before. In no time Budge had earned enough to move to his own smallholding, and is now the owner of the Monk Stretton herd of Middle Whites, prize-winners at all the shows.

Budge never forgot that Pearl was the foundation of his success. By the time she had given him eighteen litters and a dozen champions he had branched out into butchering and had his own slaughterhouse. Yet so attached had he become to his pioneering sow that he could not bear the thought of turning her into sausage meat. When decrepitude at last brought her low, he ordered his slaughterman Wildgoose to despatch her in the comfort of her own sty, and she was buried on part of Budge's land where it adjoined the churchyard. The spot is marked with a simple headstone, which reads: 'Pearl 1877–1889. Partner and Friend'.

Landlords who are forever complaining of the want of labour would do well to take a leaf out of Sir Craster Whiffle's book, and give every man a comfortable cottage and a sty in the garden, with a well-bred boar for parish use. All the talk of putting down beer-houses is not the slightest bit of use without putting something better in their place. I have encountered enough scrimshankers of one sort or another to know they have this in common – a disinclination to mend their ways unless they see some advantage in it. In Ireland they refer to their pig as 'the

Beach says Budge no longer living. Small man with a red face

gintleman what pays the rint'. What better entertainment could there be than pig-keeping for a class which falls into bad habits at the drop of a hat.

In Yorkshire they have a clear sense of what is proper. Contrast the system of prizes given for cottage pigs in the Northern counties with the rewards bestowed on a labouring man in the South. The latter may think himself fortunate to get a sovereign and a new pair of boots for thirty years' service without parish relief in Berks. or Bucks. In Yorkshire he would win as much for fourth prize in the pig class at the village show. Sir Craster Whiffle declared a fat pig to be as good an indication of the industry and sobriety of its owner as the long service valued at a pound and a pair of boots, and I agree with him.

It is enough to make a countryman's blood boil when the efforts of Sir Craster and others in promoting the cottage pig are subverted by meddlesome townsfolk. This is what Mr Oswald Pring had to say in his Report on Rural Sanitation:

> The cottage pig is a snare and delusion. Firstly it is injurious to the healthy condition of the labourer. Second, he pays more dearly for his bacon than he would if he bought it ready-made. Finally, possession of a pig creates the temptation to steal, and a labourer had best depend on his wages alone.

Monstrous what these people will say

It beggars belief that a public servant, whose expertise had hitherto been thought to lie in the inspecting of drains, should put about such dangerous falsehoods. Happily, since then the flood-tide of rebuttal has swept over Mr Pring and his report. All who know anything about pigs have united in condemning these sham-scientific delusions produced at public expense. Perhaps in future we shall hear less from Mr Pring on the subject of pigs, about which he knows practically nothing, and rather more about sewage disposal, on which he is an acknowledged authority.

Every squire and country parson that knows his duty likes to see a pig growing into money in a cottager's sty. It may not exhale the perfume of the spice-islands, but that does not trouble Englishmen brought up amid the redolences of the muck-heap. As to stealing, let these superintendents look to their own backyards. If a labouring man, rather than see his pig go short, is forced occasionally to take his opportunities where he finds them, there are worse crimes committed daily in every street in London.

Your present-day philanthropist likes nothing better than to arrange the boarding, lodging, clothing, watering, lighting and educating of every Tom, Dick and Harry along parallel lines under the inspection of Boards. Having no grasp of the principles of pig-keeping, he wishes to pursue the victims of his benevolence into their very gardens. Thus has a harmless source of pleasure and profit attracted the baleful eye of officious persons.

To put these nuisances in their place I should like to see artists of renown take for a subject the Sunday evening round the sty. It would make a picture fit to hang in any English home. There, surrounded by his young ones, is the head of the household, leaning at his ease as he smokes a Sunday pipe. By his side Mother, in best cap and shawl, holds the latest addition in her arms.

Together they mull over the manifold virtues, the form, the skin, the ears, the pork-making propensities of their pig. They weigh up the sides of bacon, to be eaten with home-grown cabbage in the months to come. While pleasantly scratching its head, Father makes the children's mouths water with the promise of black pudding, pig's fry, and the baked ham with browned potatoes they will enjoy at Christmas. Given the choice between such a painting, and the portraits of undernourished females favoured by the Royal Academy, I know which I should prefer.

The parents have no trouble persuading the tribe to nurture the source of such feasting. From the eldest lad who wheels the barrow laden with a tub of slops, to the petticoated infants toddling forth hand in hand to fetch acorns and sow-thistles, they strive mightily to please their grunting neighbour. When the time comes the meat will taste all the sweeter for the sacrifices they have made – Father by denying himself many a pint and pipe, and Mother by long hours and close economy.

Where these improving habits have taken hold, each owner expects a share of the next-door pig. Lights, chitterlings, and spare ribs are freely lent, and repaid when the borrower has something of his own for cutting. Such homely commerce gives the simple country-dweller the only bank and stock-exchange he needs. As for theatre, the final bow of a well-regarded pig is drama enough.

The arrival of the pig-sticker is the signal for the village boys to gather with a view to assisting. Well-intentioned they may be, but they make the dickens of a row and get under the feet of the specialists. They should therefore be kept as far from the sphere of action as the threat of a cuff round the ear will achieve. It might be thought there was no part in the gory business for those of the female sex. That would be to misjudge the mettle of our cottage wives. The thought of a well-stocked larder leads them to join in with a will.

Before the sticker does his duty, certain preparations are essential. The blood spurts like a burst water-main, so the valiant mistress of the house stands ready to catch it in a bucket. The family expects to dine off black puddings for days to come, and not a drop must be wasted (Mrs Timbers tells me she saves labour by part-filling the bucket with boiled oatmeal, onions, seasoning etc., and allowing the blood to gush directly into the mixture – a most sensible ploy).

The best way to remove the bristles has long been a topic for debate wherever cottage pig-keepers foregather. Some favour singeing; others hot water and a scraper. Family tradition generally decides the issue, since a man is unlikely to defy his father over first principles. In either case experi-

Ask Wellbeloved method favoured locally

menting without proper instruction is not recommended. A spoiled carcass is sure to result, and either blisters or a scalding for the perpetrator.

Those who advocate singeing build a canopy of straw over the dead pig; prevailing wind and the gauge of bristle must both be taken into account. So skilled are these thatchers that when they fire the straw, the hair is scorched, yet not a mark left on the corpse.

The exponents of the hot water method have an equal mastery of their craft. If the water is too cold the bristles will hold their ground against the scraper; if too hot, they become so firmly embedded it would take a steel rasp to get rid of them. An experienced man is said to judge the temperature by looking into the bucket. The reflection of his face tells him whether the water is ready for use. Timbers once attempted to explain to me the theory behind this phenomenon, but his insistence that 'it's the bubbles as you've to watch for' left me little the wiser. Once the water has been poured over the pig, the scraping should be done with a blunt instrument. Timbers uses the base of the pewter candle-stick by which he and Mrs Timbers light their way to bed.

Pig-meat keeps less well than that of cattle and sheep, and all organs which cannot be cured must be eaten soon after slaughter. The process of disembowelling allows the owner to pay off his debts with portions of brain, liver, kidneys, lights and sweetbreads. The creditor's meeting, attended by those neighbours who have something owing, is a far cry from any such assembly in the City. Never a top hat is to be seen, yet I swear no London money-bags getting twenty shillings in the pound had his loan redeemed with more joy than these rustic bankers.

Once the pig has been hung overnight (the church porch can be used where the cottage ceiling is too low), it is dismembered and made ready for curing as described in a later chapter. Madder-Browne undertook a study of child-birth among owners of a single pig, and noted a correlation between the slaughter in late autumn and a rise in the birthrate the following summer. What his findings signify it is difficult to say, but without a pig at the bottom of the garden the life of the rural labourer would assuredly be much the poorer.

XV
Showing

A WRITER of the old school, who went under the name of the Druid, told of finding himself in a North Country inn when the talk had turned to pig shows. They were, said one of the company, 'worth all yon horse-running business. They're twice the fun, and nobbut a fraction o' t' cost. They take up a yale afternoon, and t' Leger don't tak four minutes'.

Your plain-speaking Tyke is no fool; it is there for all to see in the way he has with a pig. At Keighley Show forty or fifty paragons of the breeder's art compete for a prize of £30. The exhibitors come from the hardy weaving class, who have forever coupled the name of Yorkshire with that of the Large White pig.

The most celebrated of the West Riding cognoscenti was Joseph Tuley, known as the originator of the Large and Middle Whites. He and Mrs Tuley lived on eighteen shillings a week, not a little of which went on pig-food. At Matchless House, the weaver's cottage they named after their celebrated sow, Tuley bred a string of champions that would not have disgraced the highest in the land. (Mrs Tuley's part in the proceedings should not be underrated. When she learned that the judge for a forthcoming show preferred a hairless pig, she borrowed Tuley's razor and gave his boar Samson as trim a shave as any barber in Jermyn Street.)

These meritorious mill-hands devote half-an-hour of their dinner-time to the sty. If it is wet they are content to sit and scratch the backs of their idols; if fine, they walk them out in the style of the family pet. Their solicitude knows no bounds. On a Saturday night the soapsuds from the weekly bath are never thrown out before they have done double-duty on the pig. If the day of the show turns cold, the best rug or blanket in the house is freely given up so the companion on whom all hopes are pinned may avoid a chill.*

After the judging the winning owner gives pride of place on the mantel of his frugal dwelling to the covetted rosette. One of these conquering heroes was asked by a representative of the *Bradford Telegraph and Argus* if he would swap his badge of honour for the velvet leg-wear of a Knight of the Garter. The reply, which had to be paraphrased for readers, was a forthright negative.

Gratified though he may be to have bested the field, the victor ludorum has merely won the approval of the judge. The Court of Errors which stands at the ringside is less indulgent. This body does not rush to acquit a pig of faults because it has found favour with an outsider. Lionizing of the winner is regarded as bad economics on the grounds that it is bound to raise the price of the offspring. The owner may thus expect from his peers many a candid reference to his pig's shortcomings, from 'graddled' back to 'mawpy' legs (dialect terms for curvilinear and splayed).

The members of the Bench make up the entire pig-keeping fraternity of the district, and their scrutiny is not confined to the duration of the show. They have followed the career of every pig from birth and know its antecedents. This prevents a practice which has plagued the show ring in other parts of the country – entering a pig in a class for which it is disqualified by age. It will readily be seen that a mature animal masquerading as a younger one would gain an advantage. The subterfuge is well-nigh impossible in the weaving community, where encyclopaedic knowledge of porcine family trees is taken as read.

Fear little chance Wellbeloved so devoted

*Such attention has perhaps only been equalled by the Prince Consort's pigman Nottage. According to Sir Craster Whiffle, on the night before a show Nottage would sleep on a truss of straw next to his charges, rising periodically to adjust their positions for ease of breathing, and perform other little offices of friendship.

We have to thank my old friend Madder-Browne for an improvement in this state of affairs. The publication of his monograph *Pig Dentition: A Guide to Age by Reference to the Incisors* settled the hash of any villain trying to palm off a two-year-old pig as a yearling. Madder-Browne, who lost a finger during his researches, compiled a table relating the development of the temporary and permanent lateral incisors to the maturity of the animal. It is advisable when making the inspection to use extreme care. Pigs resent interference in the mouth, and their reflex snapping action should be looked out for.

In his study at Pottingdean, Madder-Browne has a cabinet full of the skulls and teeth of pigs at varying stages of growth, which he is willing to show to visitors. For anyone travelling in that part of the world, it is well worth a detour. I understand that in ale-houses frequented by the desperadoes of the pig world, Madder-Browne's name has been mud since his discoveries. In that company such odium is a mark of distinction.

Well put indeed

There are no limits to which rogues will not go to steal a march on other competitors. A Birmingham manufacturer overtook a rival's pigman on the road to a show at Redditch, and sent the fellow home on the pretext that his master was dead and the pig should be scratched as a mark of respect. The supposed corpse, meanwhile, was making his way by train. At Birmingham station he noticed a crate of the first man's pigs bound for Redditch, and had it redirected to York. Each of the scoundrels arrived at the showground hoist with his own petard, and the verdict in the Pig Breeders' Club was that justice had triumphed.

My father always said Wrotterston built on similar proportions

Lord Wrotterston's sow Empress Eugénie, which weighed twelve hundredweight, two quarters and twenty-seven pounds, was the victim of fatal skullduggery the week of the Chester Show in 1888. On arrival at the station, the pigman, Nettlebed, heard her rise to her feet in the crate. He left her for a bare five minutes while attending to the other pigs, yet she was never seen alive again. It was later suspected that she was launched into eternity by chloroform. There was a theory, propagated by the Chester papers and accepted by the simple-minded, that she had been suffocated by the crowd after the crate had been deposited on the platform. How a pig protected by a large crate could be suffocated by a crowd on Waterloo Station, let alone Chester, is beyond anyone with a brain in his head.

Arriving soon afterwards, Mr Bussey, Lord Wrotterston's steward, pronounced Empress Eugénie dead. Before he could recover from the shock a group of ruffians standing nearby showed great interest in buying the carcass. Hoping to salvage something from the calamity, Bussey entered into negotiations and after much chaffering the bargain was struck at £7, well below her true value.

Bussey came to believe that foul play had occurred while the crate was still in the van. During the week of the show he noticed the purchasers presiding over a bread and bacon counter in one of the tents, and felt more than ever that they held the key to the sow's mysterious fate. The matter was sealed when Nettlebed overheard a conversation in the Moon and Cheesemonger public house. One of the culprits, clearly in his cups, spoke of paying off an accomplice at the hospital for providing the 'chlorry'. Alas, the evidence had been turned into sandwiches and eaten, and in the face of obdurate denials by the gang, the police were powerless to act.

In another case death was by natural causes, but the villain of the piece was the owner. He had a trio of capital pigs entered in the class for the Best Three in Show, but one expired before the judge arrived at the pen. The blighter propped the dead contestant between its partners, which were themselves near insensible after a substantial feed, and the judge gave them first prize. Having been foolish enough to boast about the swindle, the fellow was shunned by respectable society.

Some of our judges have been criminally slack in interpreting the standard points of the breeds. One year at the Royal the award of Best Middle White Sow went to Mistress Quickly, while the same judges gave first and second in the Large White Boar Class to her sons Narcissus and The Admiral. According to Sir Craster Whiffle, who was present, any fool could have seen they were all chips off the same block.

The farce was repeated when Arch Trespasser, belonging to Mr Wainman of Carhead, was Best Boar in the Small, Middle and Large White classes in successive years. No demurrer was lodged, in deference to Mr Wainman's high standing, but there were enough mutterings for the Committee to insist on stricter adherence to breed rules in future.

Since the white pig is not known in the wild, it sometimes happens that a champion betrays 'a touch of the tar' in later life. In a throwback to its distant ancestry, pale blue spots appear. Judges had been content to accept these markings as long as they were covered in white hairs, until the scandal at Shrewsbury involving the late Mr Natty Grindrod. His famous sow Snowflake, having beaten all-comers for two years, developed blemishes of the kind described, but was given the judges' dispensation because her bristles remained pure white.

Unfortunately for Grindrod, his former pigman Catcherside was smarting under a grievance. He had been dismissed for disputing Grindrod's opinion as to the quantity of potatoes to be consumed daily by Snowflake. In revenge Catcherside notified the authorities that the white bristles on the sow's blue spots owed more to household bleach than to nature. Snowflake was disqualified and Grindrod warned off all the major showgrounds. The absurdity of allowing parti-coloured pigs in the white classes was there for all to see, and such markings were ruled out of court.

Other swindlers have played false by means of the paint-pot. The most notorious case concerned the Berkshire boar Prince Regent at Bath. He appeared a fine animal in all points, including black pigmentation, with white flashes on the face, feet and tip of the tail. The judge had more or less

Grindrod a terrible man. Galahad heard him speak ill of Berkshire breed

determined to make him champion when, on testing the
elasticity of the tail, he found traces of white paint on his
hands. On being called to account, the owner, a bad lot
called Digweed, blamed an accidental spill during the white-
washing of his piggery. However, Prince Regent's tail proved
to be black all over, and therefore wholly inadmissable.
Digweed's guilt was as plain as a pikestaff.

Even more shocking is the disgraceful jobbery of some of
our officials. It is not unknown for the chances of success to
hang more on acquaintance with a member of the Show
Committee than on the virtues of the pig. After one bad
case, when his sow Sweet Lass of Dembleby had been beaten
by riff-raff at Norwich, Sir Craster Whiffle made his famous
bon mot at the Pig-Breeders' Club: 'Never forget that the
judge's decision is venal.' How the members roared!

Nothing exasperates your *bona fide* breeder more than
finding his pig under scrutiny by some refugee from the
poultry classes. This is the sort of thing that occurs when
members of the horse and cattle fraternity contrive to pack
the Show Committee with a bunch of nominees. Having no
interest in pigs, they hand over the judging to any Jack-in-
office who happens to be at a loose end. It is hard to credit,
but the year Sir Craster's boar Cock of the North was
entered at Banbury, the adjudication was left to a fellow
who bred Rhode Island Reds. Best in Show went to a
broken-down specimen that should have filled pork pies
years before.

It can happen that a boar, whether because of the presence
of sows in the next paddock or through the untimely workings of nature, shows evidence of over-excitation in the ring.
It is then necessary for the pigman to give the delinquent a
light tap below with his stick. This has a dampening effect,
avoiding the loss of points and sparing the blushes of by-
standers.

I remember the very thing afflicting Sir J. Trench-
Blaggard's boar Jumbo at Harrogate. The pigman, Badpenny,
was a trifle heavy-handed with his corrective action and the

Thankful to say no whisper of suspicion concerning the Empress's ~~triumphs~~

Ask Galahad explain this

boar returned the compliment. Badpenny received a nasty gash on the leg and had to be taken to the Red Cross tent for bandaging. Jumbo was disqualified under the General Conduct rule.

The year Lord Bendish's sow Puffball won the Gold Medal in Hyde Park, dereliction of duty by the pigman nearly resulted in Puffball failing to make an appearance. She had been brought up from Dorset during the week and housed in specially-prepared quarters in the basement of Bendish's house in Grosvenor Square. The pigman, Cowparsley, had orders to bed down next to her on a charpoy.

On the eve of the show Cowparsley went out and got roaring drunk, with the result that he overslept and the time for escorting Puffball across Mayfair came and went. It would inevitably have been a leisurely outing, and the catastrophe was not discovered until it was too late for the pair to reach the showground in time.

Bendish took immediate charge of the crisis, and ordered his carriage to be brought round and a ramp placed in position so that Puffball could be pushed and cajoled into the vehicle. With Bendish directing operations, the butler and footmen applied pressure from the rear, while Cowparsley entered the carriage from the other side with a bucket of beer, of which the sow was known to be fond, and enticed her in.

Soon the party were clattering along Upper Brook Street, with a speechless coachman outside, and Bendish and his pigman tending the would-be champion within. Ignoring the protests of stewards, Bendish directed the coachman to drive straight to the show ring. The London crowds, always eager for sensation and perhaps finding too little of it among the flower of English fatstock, began to follow, and the rumour went round that royalty had arrived.

As the carriage halted the other sows were being walked to their positions. The excited throng, eager for a glimpse, as they supposed, of the Prince and Princess of Wales, pressed forward. Doubts as to the royal status of the passengers began to form as Bendish emerged. His eccentricity of dress – in defiance of London convention he was wearing a suit of tweeds that had seen better days – did not accord with the crowd's preconceptions, nor did the subsequent appearance of Cowparsley clutching the bucket of beer.

Disappointment soon changed to outright partisanship when Puffball was seen to embark on a stately progress down the ramp. She entered the ring to loud huzzas and took her position among the other contestants. Sir Craster Whiffle, who was showing a pig of his own, told me there was a suspicion that the judges were swayed by the hubbub, fearing that the crowd might turn ugly if its favourite were

A fine pig being brought to show

overlooked. Be that as it may, Puffball was made champion and never was there a more popular winner. Cowparsley, who had been dismissed somewhere between Grosvenor Square and Hyde Park, was reinstated.

Galahad tells me Bendish gave up pigs a few years later and turned to sheep.
There is no accounting for some people

XVI
Temperament and
Behaviour

THE MOST fervent admirer of the pig – and I count myself as one – must doubt the claims often made for its intelligence. It was not designed for philosophizing, and can get along quite adequately without it. Even in the wild state there is little call in a pig's life for strenuous cerebration. Its particular study is to seek food, water and the society of other pigs; beyond that there is nothing to tax its brain (in avoiding attack it relies more on an instinct to run like the devil than on strategic planning).

Given such limited endeavours, it should be no surprise when a pig does exceedingly well at them. We should all be marvels if we only had three things to think about. However, the belief has grown among those prepared to swallow any flummery that the pig is some sort of genius among beasts. In my younger days a travelling sharper by the name of J. Ezard used to infest the country fairs with a succession of 'learned' pigs, to which he attributed the ability to count, answer riddles and so forth. Ezard was a long rasher of wind with rotten teeth and a habit of sucking on a foul-smoking brier, and the pigs were better specimens by far. That they were unable to perform their advertised wonders was less a reflection on them than on Ezard.

This article would lure a group of dunderheads into parting with money for the privilege of watching a pig solve arithmetical posers. He would chalk up the figures submitted by a member of the audience, and append his approximation of the total. Ezard would then bellow the question into the animal's ear, whereupon it would nod its head precisely the number of times indicated on the board.

However, it was obvious to anyone with his wits about him that whenever Ezard made a mistake in his own reckoning – a regular occurrence – the pig's calculations went astray by the same amount. The twister had clearly trained it to nod indefinitely. When he judged the desired total had been reached he would utter a cry of triumph, which the pig correctly interpreted as the signal to desist. Ezard would then expatiate on its miraculous powers. Having wasted a penny on this spectacle at the age of ten, it took me no time to spot Ezard's game. It is hard to credit, but there were people so boneheaded that they fell for it, and provided Ezard with a fraudulent living for years.

A pig will undoubtedly show a certain native shrewdness in pursuing its own interests. Sir Craster Whiffle used to tell of the time at Fetching Manor when the drayman left a dozen barrels of ale in the yard for the harvest-home supper. The pigs had been let out for an airing, and soon realized that by nudging the tap with their snouts they could start the beer flowing.

They liked what they found, and drank so much that they ended by breaking out of the yard and terrorizing the village. Sir Craster's old nurse, Aphra Bossom (his devoted 'Bossy'), was knocked down during the stampede. Finally the pigs' excesses caught up with them and they fell asleep in front of the church. It was some hours before they had sobered up enough for Sir Craster's pigman Dewlap to be able to drive them home.

Observers of the domestic pig have been mystified on occasion by the homing instinct inherited from its wild ancestor. Youatt, who was generally sound, cited the instance of a gentleman from Caversham who bought two pigs at Reading market. He turned them into his yard, but the following morning found them missing. After the hue and cry was raised a report came that they had been seen

Mercifully when some infernal nuisance – I forget who it was – poured whisky in the

swimming the Thames, which adjoined the property. Further intelligence had them trotting down the Pangbourne road, and, at a place where it is intersected, putting their snouts together as if in consultation as to the best route.

The upshot was that they returned safely to the place from which they had first been sent to Reading – a distance of nine miles. Youatt exercises himself prodigiously over the significance of this, but he had the story second-hand and was unable to cross-examine witnesses. I have heard enough tall stories to be suspicious of queer occurrences in the pig world. In particular I should like to have questioned the fellow who observed the tête-à-tête at the crossroads.

According to one of our old writers, pigs could undergo an improvement equal to that of man, but for the constraints of captivity and the short lifespan allowed to them. Sometimes ill-advised in his lust for experiment, Madder-Browne decided to put the theory to the test. He declared his intention of bringing up a young sow in such a way as to develop her whole nature. Naming her Suffragette, in acknowledgement of the part he expected her to play in pig emancipation, Madder-Browne proceeded to give his probationer the chance to show what she was capable of.

He tried as far as possible to bring up Suffragette as his own child, keeping her constantly with him, taking her for walks, allowing her to share his dining-room and so forth. At first the experiment worked well, and Madder-Browne's friends noted that Suffragette had developed qualities of attachment and *savoir-faire* beyond those found in the ordinary pig.

However, it proved impossible to train her in matters of hygiene, and as the spoilt darling of the household she grew somewhat overbearing and possessive. In her haste to claim pride of place when there was company, she would regularly send the furniture flying and break the china. Furthermore she resented it if Madder-Browne gave his attention to others, and her snappishness when piqued in this way became tiresome and even dangerous. At last he conceded that there

Empress's bran mash she was merely rendered insensible

I wonder if Whiffle too dismission here. I have heard of similar instances from most reliable people

was a point beyond which the development of the pig could not go, and that his hopes for Suffragette had far exceeded it.

Sometimes a pig will cooperate with its master in a manner that suggests the glimmerings of intelligence. Sir Craster Whiffle had a boar, Bonnie Lad, which was let out of its sty so it could be cleaned and the bedding replenished. Seeming to anticipate the purpose of his release, Bonnie Lad ran into the stable, and reappeared holding a sheaf of straw in his teeth.

The straw was intended for another purpose and was taken back into the stable. Nothing daunted, Bonnie Lad seized a later opportunity to return for his bundle and deposit it in the sty. His perseverance so impressed my uncle that thereafter Bonnie Lad was always permitted to assist Dewlap during mucking out.

Any show of acumen on the part of pigs is invariably linked to one of the modest number of objectives they set themselves, chiefly to do with food and comfort. In the southern United States it was the practice until recently to turn them into the woods, and collect them once a week for a supplement of maize and salt. The task was made simple by the scrupulous punctuality of the pigs. At the very hour at which they were to receive these favours, they would assemble from all parts as though possessed of calendar and clock.

In the backward regions of Calabria the pigs learned to answer the call of the bagpipe. Their ears being attuned to a variety of squeals during normal intercourse, one more was no doubt readily understood. At sunset the keeper would set up the chant he had taught them to recognize, and they would troop obediently homewards. Then in the morning a different caterwaul would have them hurrying to follow him to the place of feeding.

The folklore of the region has it that the use of these pipes once gave a party of pirates their come-uppance. Spying a herd of pigs foraging by the coast, they seized them and were heading off out to sea. The swineherd soon missed his charges and gave vent to a musical summons.

At the well-known sound the pigs all rushed to the side of the boat nearest the shore. The sudden concentration of a horde of porkers in one spot caused the boat to capsize and the pirates to be flung into the sea, their hopes of banquets to come sunk along with their vessel. The pigs swam back to land, and rejoined the piping herdsman none the worse for their dip.

The contrariness of pigs has been the bane of many who have not had the chance to train them in musical or other commands. Irish dockers evolved a clever method of herding pigs bound for export, which entailed driving them in the opposite direction from the boat. The pigs' natural perversity led them to turn tail and charge up the gangplank as intended.

A useful dodge in getting a reluctant pig to move forward is to tie a string to its hind leg and pull from the rear. They apply the same principle out east, according to Tradescant Lay in *The Chinese As They Are*. There, he tells us, the coolies carry swine from place to place in a species of cradle suspended from a pole.

The difficulty is to get the animal into its conveyance. This is accomplished by placing the cradle in front of the pig, and the man behind pulling its tail. In a spirit of opposition it darts forward into the required position. At journey's end the bearers dislodge their passenger by spitting in its face, a refinement we can best put down to the Chinese way of doing things.

damnable behaviour

Without a knowledge of the pig temperament, it can be the very devil to catch hold of the creatures. Sir Craster Whiffle once had a tenant named Diggory who turned out to be a double-dyed villain. He ran up a string of debts and refused to pay. It was found that he had no assets but livestock, and the bailiffs were sent down to distrain on his pigs.

It soon became apparent that these stout merchants in

bowler-hats knew nothing of the manners of the farmyard, and, with Diggory refusing to oblige, the pigs led them a merry dance round the fields. Purple-faced and perspiring, they soon gave up the chase and the pigs were spared. However, Diggory's triumph was short-lived. Sir Craster had him thrown out neck and crop.

The conduct of a pig will improve with kindness. Remove from it the struggle for survival and even the most intractable specimen will learn some manners. I have recounted the trials of Colonel Bulkinhorn, who found himself trapped in a tree by a troop of masked African boar. One of these ferocious beasts was sent to The Hague as a present for the Prince of Orange, then aged three. A masked African boar may seem an unsuitable pet for a lad of tender years, but reports of the affair are a great deal more favourable than those concerning this breed that have come out of the jungle.

Known as Erasmus for his captivating ways, the boar soon responded to his young master's attentions. He liked being stroked, and delighted in a rough brushing. When his cage was opened he came out in good humour and frisked gaily through the royal park. Sometimes, with his tail erect, he would amuse himself by chasing the fallow-deer for hours on end, though whether they enjoyed it as much may be doubted.

On one occasion, having been left alone in the courtyard by his keeper, Erasmus was found eagerly undertaking earthworks at the rear of the palace. He had made a large excavation over the sewer, which he evidently intended to reach. It was only with difficulty that Erasmus was persuaded to give up the attempt, and he is said to have expressed his disappointment by uttering a sharp cry.

A pig's most powerful urge is to dig, which can sometimes be put to good use, but is more often an infernal nuisance. Its snout is armed with a flexible cartilaginous disc, enabling it to penetrate the most brick-hard clay without a pang. Naturally a pig does not perform this chore for the fun of it, but because its keen sense of smell indicates some comestible below the surface.

The tendency is put to use by the truffle-hunters of Périgord. The tubers, which grow under trees, exude a fragrance reminiscent of a rampant boar, and the sows of the district are led into the woods to seek them out. Once their olfactories are alerted, the sows start to dig furiously. At that point the keepers take over the task themselves, but no matter how often the pigs are denied their reward, they return to the search with hopes undimmed. The poet Pope has saluted both the fungus and its pursuer with his line: 'Thy Truffles, Périgord! thy Hams, Bayonne!'

When virgin lands are brought into cultivation the pig is a ready substitute for the plough. In America its snout has made it as much of a pioneer as the frontiersman himself. How many inhabitants of Park Avenue, eating their buttered toast, stop to thank the nation's hogs for breaking up the prairie wastes? Not many, I'll be bound.

The habit can, however, lead to no end of trouble. A friend of Sir Craster Whiffle's, Mr Hector Crummhorn, had a herd of pigs which escaped overnight and dug up the graveyard in the village of Bickering-cum-Gurnaby. The vicar gave orders to the sexton to put matters to rights with the utmost haste, but he refused on the grounds that making good after an invasion by pigs fell outside his terms of employment. The sexton, a known troublemaker, was dismissed, and in order to spare bereaved relatives a sight of the desecration, the vicar was obliged to set to with the spade himself.

Mr Morison Tallboys, a protégé of the agricultural improver 'Turnip' Townshend, never kept pigs again after a case of unauthorized digging in which his life's work was ruined. His herd got out and ate the entire crop of a superior strain of turnip, which was still in the experimental stage after twenty years' study. It is said that Tallboys was so mortified he turned to rose-growing, and turnip development in this country was set back a generation.

The vocabulary of the pig has not received due attention; its 'powers of speech' have led all too many people into a footling attempt to be funny. I think particularly of a report in the *Lincoln, Rutland and Stamford Mercury*, dated 1840, which I found among Sir Craster Whiffle's papers. It told of an incident in the village of Knights Balsam.

One evening after dinner the elderly parson and his wife were alarmed by the sight of a boar peering through the open French windows, as they read aloud from *Tracts for the Times*. The pair belied their years by leaving the drawing-room a good deal faster than the boar entered it. They called for urgent assistance, and in the end little damage was done, though notes pertaining to the following Sunday's sermon had been partially chewed.

However, the correspondent of the *Lincoln, Rutland and Stamford Mercury* who signed himself 'Chatterbox', sought to enliven his report of the event by including a 'conversation' with the pig. According to this fanciful account the intruder had meant no harm, but had wished to consult the parson as to whether or not animals had souls.

'My companions and I were discussing the matter,' the pig was quoted as saying, 'and a difference of opinion developed between those who held that there was no reason why they should not, and others who thought the idea patently absurd. I volunteered to seek advice from the best authority, but my visit to the vicarage was, alas, misinterpreted.' The pig was said to have apologized for damaging the notes, which he had been studying for any guidance they might offer.

It remains a puzzle as to why Sir Craster should have wanted to keep this fable. I can only conclude that he knew some of the principles involved. As a rule he had no time for buffoonery.

In more serious vein I have attempted to compile, I believe for the first time, a 'dictionary' of the grunts and other utterances of the pig, with their meanings in porcine discourse. I am indebted to Mr Walter Treadgold of the

Natural History Museum for putting the various articulations into phonetic form. He has already done the same for bird-song – his 'fitz-e-deu, fitz-e-deu, bubble-na-na-na' of the marsh tit being a characteristically happy likeness.

To the pig, dissimulation is an unknown art; the noises it makes leave other pigs, and anyone within earshot, in no doubt as to its state of mind:

Threat call: A short, barking 'khaargk', as if testily clearing the throat. A signal for any bystander to leave the vicinity by the shortest available route.

Full-blooded attack: A stentorian roar, which Mr Treadgold has interpreted as 'gggghaaaaaoo-ghnoo-ghnoo-ghnoo-ghnoo-ghnoogk'.

Fear: Shakespeare's 'weke! weke! so cries a pig prepared for the spit' is condemned as feeble by Mr Treadgold, who prefers a keening 'quiiiieeeekh, quiiiieeeekh'.

Pain: Similar to the above, the volume and duration increased by a factor of ten.

Impatience when kept waiting for food: A furious 'quee-wee-wee', rising in intensity as the trough is filled.

Feeding: a muted 'ghwoosh, ghwoosh, ghwoosh'.

Sow summoning piglets to feed: A rapid, snuffling 'phghwoo-phghwoo, phghwoo-phghwoo'.

Contentment: Mr Treadgold believes the oft-used 'oink' altogether lacks the richness of the actual sound. After much thought he renders the grunt of a pig at ease as 'nghawghghnk'.

Empress emits habitual 'sssiiiiiilhuh' when sleeping. Write Treadgold

XVII
Uses of the Pig

MEMBERS of the Pig-Breeders' Club can enjoy a witticism with the next man, so long as it does not overstep the mark. One that went the rounds at the club, and was judged to be exceptionally droll, concerned an American farming magnate who was visiting Lobb the bootmaker for a pair of bluchers. 'Where I come from,' he told the man fitting him, as though vouchsafing something that was not known to every boy in breeches, 'we use the whole of a pig, bar the squeak.'

The bootmaker, to whom the saying was as familiar as a cobbler's awl, replied: 'We use that too, sir'. It was agreed by members that the riposte was as good as anything you would get at the Gaiety. I only wish Sir Craster Whiffle had been alive to hear it. How he would have laughed!

I have not introduced this pleasantry merely to entertain. One should not forget the moral to the story, viz that the pig earns its keep more than any creature living, by its multiple uses. Without question the one nearest to an Englishman's heart is its contribution to the table, and it is with that that I begin this summary.

The meat of the pig has been considered a delicacy ever since some ingenious fellow invented the spear. The recipes of Mrs Hyssop, which I introduce later, were not available to prehistoric diners, but I have no doubt they made the most of a stuck pig and a camp fire. I have done the same myself out east, and there is something about pork roasted

Told Galahad he had heard it elsewhere

under the heavens which beats anything that the Café Royal can do.

Seekers after sensation will go to great lengths to dress up a meat which in my view needs no improvement. The Romans are said to have fed their pigs on dried figs and honeyed wine to enrich the flavour (apart from being unnecessary it would not be an economic proposition today, with the iniquitous burden of tax borne by the propertied class).

Whiffle absolutely right about this

In the case of the dish *Porcus Trojanus* their elaborations would stick in the gullet of any honest-to-God Englishman. It consisted of a hog roasted whole, stuffed with thrushes, larks, beccaficos, nightingales and oysters, and served with wine gravy. The high living of these Roman trenchermen was such that sumptuary laws had to be passed to curb their extravagance.

For reasons I have never fathomed, the Jewish and Mussulman faiths proscribe this meat altogether, while other religions have made it the centre of attention. Until missionaries put them right on such matters, the Otaheitans of the South Seas offered their deities roast pork as the most savoury and acceptable act of worship they could perform. Now, I understand, they sing hymns and eat the pork themselves. It is a half leg to a piece of neck end that they are all the better for it.

Opinions differ regarding the pig meat to be found in another of the distant regions of the earth, the South American jungle. Some find it revolting; others cannot speak too highly of it. Among the latter was General Gripperfield, who has left an account of hunting peccary up the River Berbice. Having surprised a party of these wild swine, Gripperfield was charged by the leading boar, with teeth clashing and bristles standing up like a bed of nails. One of the best shots of his day, he despatched the attacker with a single bullet, and the rest of the tribe made off at high speed.

Gripperfield sent his party in pursuit, for the purpose of replenishing their larder. Confident of being in no danger, he laid aside his gun and sat down on an abandoned anthill. Suddenly he heard a commotion in the thickets, and the howling and clattering of teeth left him in no doubt as to what it was. Without realizing, the hunters had sent the herd in a full circle back towards the General. Quite unarmed, he had barely time to take refuge in the nearest popatacuanha tree before the peccaries hurtled over his erstwhile resting place, and were lost to view.

Gripperfield gave his men the dressing-down of a lifetime for allowing the beasts to double back on themselves, and put him within an inch of his life. He then set them to preparing the evening's repast from the specimen he had shot. Gripperfield swears it was the finest pork he had ever tasted, and spends a paragraph on his regret at no longer being able to eat peccary since he left the Caribbean station.

One can only think that Gripperfield's adventures had affected his judgement, as anyone who has tasted this meat will confirm. The peccary has a gland in the middle of the loins, which can be seen by parting the bristles that cover it. This exercise is by no means pleasant, and is indeed unnecessary, since even without investigation the gland secretes a fluid which would wrinkle the nostrils of a skunk. The stench is used by the peccary to deter its predators, I should imagine with great success, and it gives the meat a disagreeable taint. I feel sure that a sampling in less dramatic circumstances would have soon changed Gripperfield's opinion.

Another type of pig with holds no attraction for English palates is the Chinese. Useful though it was in developing our native animal to its present state of perfection, the pure-bred Chinese has a shining, flabby appearance on the plate which would spoil the appetite of a starving man. I remember Sir Craster Whiffle once likened it to baked jellyfish. Tradescant Lay tells us that when cut in long rashers and dried in the sun, this meat is not quite so offensive, though indistinguishable from dog or cat similarly treated. I am ready to take his word for it.

According to the writer Charles Lamb we are indebted to the Chinese for discovering the merits of roast pork. However, he wraps his account in such a deal of flim-flam that a plain man must entertain serious doubts about it. Working from an old manuscript he claims to have seen (whether in the original Chinese he does not say), Lamb informs us that a swineherd, Ho-ti, one day left his house in the care of his son Bo-bo. To cut an interminable story short, Bo-bo burns the place down through carelessness, inadvertently roasting a litter of pigs in the process.

The wrath of the father turns to gratification when he tastes the pork, and the rest of this author's ramblings tell how every dwelling in the neighbourhood is soon going up in flames, as the inhabitants discover the secret. The arson continues until a sage appears, compared by Lamb to the philosopher Locke, who points out that a pig can be roasted just as well without firing the house.

The following will give some idea of the author's style: 'There is no flavour comparable, I will contend, to that of the crisp, tawny, well-watched, not over-roasted, crackling, as it is called – the very teeth are invited to their share in the pleasure of this banquet in overcoming the coy, brittle resistance – with the adhesive, oleaginous – O call it not fat – but an indefinable sweetness growing up to it – the tender blossoming of fat – fat cropped in the bud – taken in the shoot – in the first innocence . . .' I recommend those who can stomach more of this to turn to the original.

A literary man equally not to my taste is the French poet Verlaine. My interest was roused when I learned that Verlaine had spent some time as a schoolmaster at Stickney, near Boston, where he had acquired a taste for chine cooked after the Lincolnshire fashion (this recipe is given later). I glanced at a volume of his poems in translation, hoping for some reference to old Lincolnshire memories, but was sadly disappointed. Instead of sound sentiments such as he would have encountered at Stickney, I found the subject matter infected by much unhealthy French sighing and moping.

It came as no surprise to learn that Verlaine had at one time consorted with M. Rimbaud, a poet of similar type, and had been clapped in gaol for shooting at him. My native county can be thankful that this disreputable alien was a bird of passage. It is clear we were well rid of him.

Sir Craster Whiffle was so fond of pork pies that he never went on a journey without one. He had a special case made, which was designed to accommodate the pie and protect the glazed pastry from damage (he had a horror of crumbs). The pork pie has long been a favourite of all ranks of society, and is made in every size from 1lb. to 20lb. The smallest are generally purchased at railway stations, while the 3lb. version is destined for the higher class of customer. The very largest pies are consumed in great numbers at the universities.

The eating habits of English people have changed much in recent times, not always for the better. In a more vigorous age there was none of your milk-and-water turkey meat at Christmas, but a boar's head, ushered in with a chorus to be found in *Ritson's Ancient Songs*:

> Be gladde now, both more and lasse,
> For this hath ordeyned our stewarde,
> To cheere you all this Christmasse,
> The bore's head with mustarde.

Would have similar trouble with Connie

I would like to revive this practice at Longwindley, but I cannot persuade Mrs Whiffle to my opinion.

In a custom which is also, alas, no longer followed, the Abbot of St Germain, in Yorkshire, was bound once a year to send a present of a boar's head to the hangman. It coincided with the feast of St Vincent, and in processions on that day the executioner took precedence over the monks. I know many readers will join me in regretting that these quaint old observances have been allowed to lapse.

The Pig-Breeders' Club is one of the few places where a boar's head is still served whole (when Sir Craster Whiffle put me up for the Athenaeum I naturally deferred to his wishes, but 'the Trough', as it is known among clubmen, is my 'home from home' when in London). Umbridge, our chef, has first to remove the skull before pickling and stuffing can be undertaken. Having sewn round the neck, he boils the head for a few hours, allows it to cool and then glazes it. On President's Night Umbridge does several of these heads, each with an orange in its jaws. The man is an artist, of that there is no doubt.

In the ordinary way a pig's head is split before salting, the upper portions being known in the butchering trade as eye-pieces, and the lower as chaps or chawls. When in the West country I make a point of ordering Bath chaps, a speciality of the region. The curing process used locally seems to impart a notably succulent flavour to the chap.

In his *Treatise on Swine* (1814), Henderson claims to have invented the smokehouse used by the curers. Like many a good idea it derived from the endless bother he had under the old system. Henderson would cart his hams and flitches round the cottages of the district, and pay the occupants a few pence to hang them first in the chimney, then elsewhere in the house until he could collect them. What with salt scattering all over the place, and hams falling on the children's heads, Henderson found himself forever handing out ribbons, tobacco etc. in order to make peace with the injured parties. This benefactor duly contrived his own smokehouse, which has since been copied round the world.

I will not trouble readers with advice on preparing the standard cuts of meat, with which their cooks will be thoroughly familiar. However, it is my firm intention to neglect no aspect of the pig, alive or dead. I thus turn to some of the old country dishes which have long been a staple of the labouring class.

Mollycoddled townsfolk make an unholy fuss about the innards of a pig, but I have no time for such daintiness. There is much good eating to be had from well-seasoned viscera. In compiling this selection of homely comestibles, I have been helped by Mrs Hyssop of Woodhall Spa. For some years she has contributed recipes to the *Lindsey and Kesteven Pig-Breeder*, which can be found in her book, *From a Lincolnshire Kitchen*.

Black pudding: A bacon pig will shed eight pints of blood, which should be agitated or it will stick like fish-glue. A mixture of pearl barley or groats, flour, onions, leaf-fat and seasoning should be already prepared, so the blood may be added at once (it will be remembered that Mrs Timbers places the ingredients in the bucket before she catches the blood of the stuck pig).

Cut a section of the large gut, tie it at one end, and blow into it in case of punctures. Funnel the mixture into its casing and tie the other end, leaving a thread long enough to hang over the edge of the pan. Cook for twenty minutes in hot water (do not boil or the skin will burst and wreck the whole operation). To ascertain if it is ready, pull the pudding out by means of the thread and pierce it with a pin. If the blood runs through, replace it till the blood coagulates; when properly cooked the pudding should be firm to the touch. Wipe off the red scum and rub with a small piece of fat to improve the appearance. It is capital served cold at a picnic, but nothing keeps out the chill so well on a winter's morning as sliced black pudding fried in lard.

Chitterlings: Trim the small intestine away from its fatty surroundings, and empty the contents. Slice lengthways and scrape off the muscular coating and internal mucus. Pickle for twelve hours in brine flavoured with coriander, thyme and bay. Cut the chitterlings up fine, and introduce them into a casing of large gut as with black pudding. After heating, place the sausage in brine for three weeks, and then suspend it in a smoking chimney for a fortnight. Chitterlings are a nourishing stand-by for the thrifty labourer who has no money to throw about.

Stomach: Clean carefully, treat with salt for a day or two to sweeten, and continue as with chitterlings. Filled with cheap cuts, well minced, it is another boon for the poor.

Haslets, or pig's fry: In the same category as the above. Chop the heart, lungs, crow and skirts (the diaphragm and other membranes). Mix with onions or apples, and fry. In Lincolnshire currants and spice are added to make a filling for pastry turnovers.

Sausages: There are grounds for supposing that all kinds of material are sold in the name of sausage. Horseflesh is perhaps the least repugnant of those which the maker does not choose to advertise. Everything from vermin to the occasional butcher's finger is said to have found its way into this form of food, and Mrs Whiffle has orders never to allow a bought sausage in the house. It is a simple matter for Cook to make large quantities by adapting the methods used for black pudding and chitterlings.

Skin: Simmer for several hours, skim, and use the result for jellies.

Flead cakes: After the rendering of lard, the remaining fatty membranous tissue forms a brown, crackly leaf or flead. These scratchings (as they are known) should be mixed with salt, water and 1lb. of flour to make a paste. Roll out, sprinkle more flead, fold over, and roll again. Continue the process until the paste is half-an-inch thick. Cut into rounds, fold over, brush with an egg and bake. I find a bag of flead cakes most sustaining when out shooting in an east wind.

Lardy Johns: My early morning appetizer. Rub a quarter of a pound of home-rendered lard into half a pound of flour. Add baking powder, currants, sugar and water. Roll out, cut into two-inch squares and bake.

Lincolnshire chine: Soak the chine for twelve hours. Score both sides, and fill the scorings with a paste of flour, water, parsley, thyme, marjoram, spring onions and raspberry leaves. Cover the chine with a flour and water crust, and bake. It says something for the poet Verlaine that, when served this old Lincolnshire dish at his lodgings in Stickney, he commented favourably and asked for a second helping.

Trotters: Simmer in vegetable stock, and serve in brown

Too bad Connie won't permit this

or white sauce. A savoury variant is to dip the stewed trotter in egg, cover in breadcrumbs and fry.

Brains: Fry in batter to make brain fritters. A fixture on the breakfast table at Longwindley.

Lincolnshire brawn: Stew half a head, two hocks and two trotters with sage. When the meat comes away from the bones, remove it and return the bones to the liquor. Chop the meat, tongue and skin, add salt, saltpetre, pepper and nutmeg, and mix with the strained liquor. Place in a wetted mould.

Hog's pudding: Stuff a section of gut with tripe, suet, oatmeal and seasoning. Sir Craster Whiffle used to distribute hog's pudding to the poor of the neighbourhood at Christmas.

I trust that Mrs Hyssop's suggestions will encourage readers to try these flavoursome parts of the pig, which are persistently ignored by other writers on cookery.

No account of this kind would be complete without a reference to lard. The leaf or kidney fat is chilled, chopped up, and rendered by fire or steam heat. The molten lard is then separated, clarified, and run off into casks or tins. There are three qualities of lard: the first sold for domestic use; the second used in the manufacture of oil; and the third, prepared from inferior meat trimmings and tainted fat, forms one of the constituents of soap and perfumery.

Lard oil is often used as an 'improver' in olive, spermaceti and other oils. It is derived by placing quantities of fat in woollen bags and subjecting them to a pressure of a hundred tons for fifteen hours. Witherspoon tells us that the city of Cincinnati manufactures the laudable total of one-and-a-half million gallons of lard oil annually. Residues from the process are put to an industrial use with which I am not familiar; for amplification I refer readers to the pamphlet *Pig's Bounty: The Benefits of Lard* by Sanders Spencer.

The bristle is yet one more of the myriad gifts bestowed on humanity by pigs. Such is the demand by our brush-makers that a thousand tons are imported into the country each year. This has been calculated by Madder-Browne as representing a total of 17,554,892,731 individual bristles. Most come from Russia, where the animals are fed on refuse from the tallow factories. It is thought to impart to the bristles their special strength and elasticity. The natives of rock-bound Scottish islands use a rope fabricated from pig bristle when they hang from the perilous cliff-top, in search of gulls' eggs. They say it is less likely to fray than hempen rope. Few of us, I fancy, would dispute the matter with a man who makes a habit of leaning over precipices.

It only remains to point out the value of bones and feet in glue-making; blood as fertilizer; glands for medical purposes; the skin for leather goods; and the bladder for plugging leaks in drains. In contending that there is a use for everything bar the squeak, I rest my case.

XVIII
Of Pigs and Men

A MONG the most remarkable sows that ever lived was
one belonging to Sir H. Mildmay. Slut, as she became
known after rolling in a bog, was trained by Sir Henry's
gamekeeper, Toomer, to point and find game. Toomer had
been dissatisfied with his own pointer, and had decided to
make a sporting pig of Slut. Her nose was better than any
dog, and she sometimes stood a jacksnipe when the other
pointers had passed it by. She was known to stand a single
partridge at forty yards.

It was a curious thing that the dogs were jealous of Slut,
and did not like to hunt when she was with them. However,
Toomer employed her for several years, until the death of
Sir Henry. She was then sold at auction for a large sum of
money, but the secret of breaking swine to the field remained
with her old keeper, and Slut's pointing days were over.
Her instincts did not entirely desert her, for she was later
held responsible for a number of missing chickens.

The training of pigs has taken many a strange turn.
According to Youatt, a farmer of the old breed drew crowds
at St Albans when he entered the market-place in a small
chaise-cart, drawn by four hogs at a brisk trot. They were
then driven to the woolpack yard, unharnessed, and regaled
with a trough of beans and mash. A gentleman wanted to
give £50 for the concern as it stood, but the offer was
declined with vigour. Stating that he had not spent six

months training a team of pigs in order to sell them to the first applicant, the eccentric coachman drove off to roars from the crowd.

A pig will form the unlikeliest attachments if thrown together with other creatures. A landowner in Fife, Sir Murdo McBawdie o' the Drains, had a sow which became the perpetual companion of his dog Butcher. Both would accompany Sir Murdo on walks of five or six miles. The dog was fond of swimming and the sow soon followed suit. If anything was thrown in the water for Butcher, she would dispute the prize with him. The two shared the same kennel, and when Butcher died, the sow pined so grievously she was not far behind him.

Pigs are opportunists, and given the chance will take over the household. Sir Craster Whiffle knew a woman in the north of the county who bought a pig, Nipper, to deal with garden refuse. Nipper was adopted by the maid, Annette, and became her darling. Finding his visits to the kitchen winked at, he was soon basking full length before the fire. If put out in the yard, Nipper would kick up such a hullaballoo, thumping with his snout at the kitchen door, that she was obliged to let him in again.

Nipper was often to be seen standing guard over Annette as she performed her household duties, and seemed to be watching the proceedings with a sagacious air. However, the idyll could not last. When Annette took a position elsewhere, her replacement had no taste for the society of pigs. Many were the swipes with a broom Nipper received at the kitchen door, before he retired to his sty to contemplate the injustice of life.

Of all creatures pigs are held to be the most susceptible to music. Old Farmer Tallybutt, a Lincolnshire worthy I recall from boyhood, had a pet sow called Beauty, which went everywhere with him. At village fêtes and flower shows, if he lost track of Beauty, he would invariably find her near the bandstand, giving every appearance of following the recital.

Trepanning's view on this entirely justified

In Mexico, according to Bullock, landowners hired Indian youths to sing to their herds. The carolling of these lads lulled the senses of their charges, who were thought to gain weight as a result of eupepsia engendered by the music.

The Mexican custom of naming pigs after politicians was brought to this country by the Cornish peer Lord Trepanning. After what he considered to be the Liberal party's treasonable attack on the House of Lords, he registered his Large Black boar in the name of Campbell-Bannerman. Few would have known of this barb, had not Trepanning revealed it on a rare visit to Westminister. When asked to withdraw by the Lord Chancellor, Trepanning contended that any apology should be directed towards the pig. Never perhaps cut out for public life, he returned to his estates and was lost to politics.

It is many years since the House of Lords was startled at a speech by the then Bishop of Lincoln, concerning a scandal in the diocese. Older readers will recall that the Revd Osborn Purfoy, vicar of Great Gimping, bigamously married two members of the same family, while also pursuing an entanglement with the organist's wife. Rumours of the affair had swept the county, and such was the disquiet that the Bishop felt obliged to make the facts public.

It may well be asked what place this unsavoury business has in a book about pigs. The answer is that the Bishop, who kept a herd of Lincolnshire Curly Coats at the palace, was an old friend of Sir Craster Whiffle's. On the day of the Bishop's speech, Sir Craster, with his unfailing tact and diplomacy, was able to help him out of a tight corner.

By a longstanding arrangement, both were guests that evening at a dinner in Stamford given by the Lincolnshire Stalwarts. As soon as the Bishop arrived, he was surrounded by a small army of Stalwarts, muttering 'bad business' and trying to pump him about Purfoy. Sir Craster, who was standing nearby, saw what he must do. 'Tell me, Bishop,' he thundered. 'Do you prefer wet meal, or dry?'

The Stalwarts, none of them countrymen, briefly pre-

tended an interest in pig-feed, but by the time the Bishop
and Sir Craster had moved on to the respective merits of
turnips and swedes, all had melted away. As long as I knew
him, Sir Craster had an exceptional gift for shaking off
unwanted company.

The Bishop was once the victim of a calamitous printing
error in the *Lincoln, Rutland and Stamford Mercury*. During a
sermon he had singled out members of the congregation
who did not confine their attendance at the Cathedral to
Sundays. 'With such individuals, worshipping merely once a
week is not enough', he observed. 'For those who require
more, it is both the duty and delight of the Dean and
Chapter to administer it daily.'

It was the practice of the *Mercury* to report the Bishop's
sermons at length. On this occasion the word 'horsewhip-
ping' was inadvertently substituted for 'worshipping'. The
slip resulted in a meaning opposite to that intended, and
was the cause of many ruffled feathers in the diocese. Sir
Craster told me that the Bishop, whose boar Archdeacon
was Best in Show at Newark the same week, quite had his
pleasure spoiled by the incident.

The basis of successful breeding lies in the partnership of
owner and pigman. Sir Craster Whiffle often referred to
himself as the conductor, and Dewlap as his first violin.
Timbers and I have had our disagreements – notably over
the constituents of bran mash – but we see eye-to-eye on
what matters most, viz the onward march of the Longwindley herd. Any serious falling out is sure to be attended by
disaster, as the following example shows all too clearly.

The Birmingham manufacturer Mr Cuthbert Farthingale,
proprietor of Farthingale's Bearings, acquired a large estate
in Worcestershire and established a herd of prize-winning
pigs by the simple expedient of buying them. He had attracted one of the finest pigmen in the country, Weovil,
who had been with Sir Heneage Rutter (it was rumoured
that he had offered Weovil an extra five shillings a week,
and other benefits such as Sunday afternoon off).

*Timbers seems
an excellent
man.
Wellbeloved
good with
the Empress
but I could
wish his
manner less
offensive*

The trouble started when Farthingale ordered a set of silver troughs, inscribed with his new family crest (a cluster of ball bearings, with crossed trotters, and the motto '*Honoro ferrum et porcum*'). Weovil refused to regard the polishing of the troughs as part of his duties, and the butler was pressed into service on pain of dismissal. The upshot was that both men left Farthingale's employement, the replacement pigman proved to be better at polishing silver than looking after pigs, and the herd went into a decline. The episode was regarded as a warning against placing self-aggrandisement above harmony in the piggery.

The pigman is often thought of as a slow-thinking rustic, but he is not short of an apt rejoinder when tried beyond endurance. One that caused many a smile at the Pig-Breeders' Club was provoked by an owner who was new to pig-keeping. He believed that all he needed to know was to be found in books, and lectured his pigman interminably on the 'doctrine' of this author or that. Finally he wearied the poor fellow once too often. Handing in his notice, he told his master he was the one who needed 'doctorin''. Members of the club dined out on that for years.

Sir Craster Whiffle's pigman Dewlap was of the old school. He was one of the last exponents in Lincolnshire of the 'pig magic', a type of mumbo-jumbo used in former times during the serving of the sows. It was handed down with much secrecy from father to son, as a way of guarding their employment. When Sir Craster was in attendance, Dewlap would mutter the formula in his beard so as not to be overheard. It was credited with increasing the number in a litter, but the evidence was against it. Dewlap's successor, Stopes, achieved a fecundity with pigs unmatched in the East of England, and yet scorned such practices.

To say that Stopes succeeded Dewlap, while to all intents and purposes true, is to overlook the brief interregnum of Diligence Trugg. After a reading of John Stuart Mill's *The Subjection of Women*, Sir Craster had decided to strike a blow for equality by appointing a pigmaid. Diligence began well,

Tell Galahad

Told Galahad. He knew it from another source

but allowed success to go to her head. The novelty of a female in the show ring attracted attention, and when the usual prizes came the way of Sir Craster's pigs, newspaper reports would have it that it was all the work of their new attendant.

Diligence responded to fame by becoming a trial to her employer and others. She began to dress unsuitably for someone required to handle pigs, and complained of her dresses becoming soiled. When she called Sir Craster's head ploughman, Agar, an old fool, it was time to bring the experiment to a speedy conclusion.

I close this section with an account of some of the outstanding pigs produced by Mr Wainman of Carhead. Lord of the Wassail, the first of the Middle White Breed ever to take a prize at the Royal, had a coat of hair eight inches long. Many a sporting fish fell foul of this Esau among pigs. On Wharfe or Spey, Wainman invariably used a fly constructed from Wassail's fleece.

Fresh Hope beat everything for bulk. When she was sold for 20 guineas and yielded up her harms to the butcher, they weighed 94lb. each. Those who saw the salted remains declared that, but for being almost all 'good sandwich meat', they might have belonged to a hippopotamus. Wainman's pigman, Pocket, swore he once saw Fresh Hope's ghost walking in stately fashion through the yard and into her former sty. When he went to investigate, the old champion had vanished without trace.

For thickness of hide no pig came up to Carhead Duke. At slaughter it was found that his skin would only do for blacksmiths' aprons. However, as it would not make three, and to cut it up for two would be a criminal waste, it was turned into a partition wall for a taproom in Keighley. In that position it is made the text of much discussion on pigs, and is always alluded to with respect.

Arch Trespasser was buried six foot deep in the Carhead Stack garth, with a silver ring in his nose. It had no hallmark, since it was privately made. One may imagine the

Monica Simmons, a charming girl, knew what she was doing. Terrible habit calling Empress the piggy wiggy

Admiring pigs at the Xmas fatstock show.

archaeologists of Yorkshire having some trouble as to the ring's date and purpose, when a century hence they invade Arch Trespasser's borrow with their pickaxes.

A pig once escaped from Waiman's yard in the hard winter of 1865. The River Aire had frozen over, and while fleeing the rescue party the unfortunate creature fell through the ice and drowned. There was no thaw for many weeks, and skaters could clearly see the corpse amid the glacial mass. When its bristles appeared above the surface in a temporary mild spell, it was taken as a warning not to skate.

The champion sow Silverwing showed the light offal head of the silver strain to perfection. She won nearly thirty prizes off malt dust and turnips. In the end she went in the loins and hams, and became lumpy, as pigs will when they are brought to show once too often. She was by King of the West, as was her constant partner, King Cube. Wainman smoked many a cigar in contemplation of this beautiful pair, when he did not care to look at anything else.

Wainman clearly a man after my own heart. One's life eternally plagued by people wanting me to do this that and the other. The Empress a great comfort and I sometimes think the only sane resident of Blandings, apart from myself.

XIX
The Pig in Art,
War and Peace

THE Pig Breeders' Club is fortunate in possessing the finest collection of pig portraiture and statuary in the country. As one enters from Brook St, on the left is the bronze of Lively, winner of many prizes for a former president of the 'Trough', Sir Cato Hitch. Standing barely an inch off the ground, Lively was as broad as she was long. In life she had a habit of cocking her head as if about to speak, which the artist has caught to perfection. More than once I have seen members arrive at the club, and quite involuntarily respond by wishing Lively a good morning.

When recounting the history of the pig for the benefit of visitors, I show them the charming display to the right of the club entrance. Here one may study the development of the species through its chief glory: the hindquarters. To pause before Wedderburn's *Pigs Through the Ages*, done in plaster of Paris, is to marvel at the work of our forebears in fashioning the bounteous hams we know today.

Wedderburn's forest boar has the great shoulders and lissom flanks to be found in the wild animal. As he progresses from the dawn of domestication to our modern breeds, we see the bulk steadily deserting the cheaper regions at the front, and consolidating in those behind which fetch 1s. 6d. a pound. Every breeder counting his guineas on market day can thank the great men who shaped our English pig.

In the principal rooms of the club hang portraits of pigs of all kinds. When I go to the smoking room after dinner, for old times' sake I take a chair near the painting of Dame Fortune, a sow of Sir Craster Whiffle's. When Dame Fortune was sitting for the artist, a curious instance of jealousy occurred. A sow who had lived on good terms with her for years seemed to resent her own exclusion from the picture. At any rate, with a sudden sideways movement of the head, she gave the easel holding the half-finished likeness a deliberate nudge.

Before the artist could save it, the canvas had fallen face-down in the mud. He had no choice but to start afresh, once the disobliging sow had been banished to another sty. The outcome was presented to the club by Sir Craster, and Dame Fortune looks down on the post-prandial scene in a spirit of solidarity that is a joy to behold.

There was a great to-do in the art world when Lord Soke decided to make some changes at Gorlestone, his ancestral seat in Sussex. Soke, of course, was an outstanding pig-breeder who won prizes at the Royal every year between 1859 and 1892. In the previous century a forebear had hired a jobbing French painter, name of Laguerre, to decorate the ballroom, drawing room and so forth. The fellow had plastered the walls and ceilings with classical scenes, many of which were as far-fetched as these things very often are.

Soke knew of an artist in the village who made a living painting farmyard scenes. There was generally a pig or two grubbing about, and livestock to suit every taste, and they were in great demand in the neighbourhood. Some of the cherubs on the walls at Gorlestone were frankly surplus to requirements, and Soke conceived the idea of getting this man Edwin Meek to paint over a few and replace them with pigs. Naturally he specified his own breed, the Middle White, which being pink would have fitted well with the abundance of human flesh already there.

Somehow the word got round, and the president of the Royal Academy very nearly had a fit. He telegraphed Soke

Portrait of Empress by Freddie's man Breamworthy quite terrible. Must find another painter.

I cannot think Soke had any sisters. I should never have heard the last of it from Connie

begging him to let the plan go no further. Of course, with his experience, Meek could paint pigs like a monkey cracking nuts, and he had half-a-dozen completed while the Royal Academy was composing the telegram. Finally the president himself arrived at Gorlestone, bearing a letter from the Surveyor of the Queen's pictures. It was bruited that on seeing Meek's work he remarked: '*C'est magnifique, mais ce n'est pas Laguerre*', though there is some doubt as to whether he had it in him.

Soke was not the sort of man to be dictated to on home ground, or anywhere else. However, Queen Elizabeth had spent a night at Gorlestone during a progress in the South, and the letter from the Palace carried enough weight for him to give Meek an honourable discharge. The Academy sent down a restorer to remove what he had been able to accomplish in the time. While I bow to the experts on the subject of Laguerre, there was more than enough of his handiwork for those who like it, and I think it is a great pity Meek was not given the opportunity to win his spurs.

Among the books from Sir Craster Whiffle's library, now in my possession, is one in the Flemish language by van der Neck. My cousin Ernest Whiffle, who is a linguist, translates the title as *The Pig: Breeding, Rearing and Killing* (*De Varken: Fokken, Verzorgen, Schlachten*).

Alas, I can make nothing of the text, but there is an illustration of great artistic interest. It shows the collection of death masks assembled by a Flanders breeder, Zacharias van Loon. After the slaughter of a favourite pig, van Loon always made a plaster cast of the head for posterity; when he died they were placed on display in the museum at Ghent. I have promised to take Mrs Whiffle to see this phenomenon as soon as the present hostilities in Europe are over.

Mention of the events of 1914, still unfolding as I write, brings me to a serious omission in newspaper accounts of the causes of the conflict. There has been no recognition of the part played by pigs in the affair. The assassination of

Death of the Empress too awful to contemplate. Consider getting man to make plaster cast for portrait gallery

Archduke Franz Ferdinand can be directly traced to the banning of Serbian pigs by Austria-Hungary in the tariff dispute of 1906; yet I have looked in vain for any reference to it.

The facts are as clear as daylight. Obliged to dispose of their pigs in distant markets, the Serbs entered the tinned meat trade; but they were checkmated when Bosnia-Herzegovina, their outlet to the sea, was smartly annexed by the imperial government in Vienna. I need not trouble readers with the subsequent huffing and puffing between the two sides, which culminated in the demise of the Archduke at Sarajevo. The details are too well known. However, for the benefit of historians, the decisive role of pigs at the start of the friction must not go unrecorded.

Had no idea of this

My task is now completed, but I feel I cannot end with the pig as a harbinger of war; it would not be just. Indeed the very opposite is the case. Many have testified to the pacific and restorative effect pigs have had upon them when life has become burdensome. Madder-Browne, for example, is a martyr to neuralgia, particularly when frustrated during experimental work. Naturally excitable by temperament – I have known him throw a Bunsen burner the length of the laboratory – he finds a visit to the pig-yard is balm to his nerves.

The manufacturer of phonographs, Mr Frederick Schwab of Connecticut, has taken this principle a step further. He persuaded engineers of the Schwab Sound Corporation to capture the grunts and wheezes of his sows on wax cylinder (they are thought to be the first animals ever heard through mechanical agency).

So interesting have one's experiences confirmed by others. Whiffle an unfailing inspiration

I have before me a clipping from the *New York Times*, kindly sent from America, which tells of this marvel. On his travels Mr Schwab takes a phonograph and his collection of cylinders with him. At the end of a long day devoted to trade, he retires to his room to be reminded by this rustic medley of the pigs he has left behind. He states that, though he has personally supervised the recording of Signor

Caruso, and admires him greatly, it is to the sounds of the farmyard that he turns first for solace.

I am seldom out of sorts (Mrs Whiffle has often remarked on the fact), but I never approach the sties at Longwindley without a lifting of the spirits. Sir Craster used to say – I can hear him now! – that the sight of pigs with their noses in the trough did a man more good than any Methodist sermon there ever was. Following his precept, I am invariably to be found among my herd at feeding time. There is much to be learned from the pig in pursuit of what it loves best. The sound of a hundred hearty eaters making short work of their rations tells me in the plainest terms what I most wish to know: that all is well.